METAL IONS
IN
AQUEOUS SOLUTION

THE PHYSICAL INORGANIC CHEMISTRY SERIES

Robert A. Plane and Michell J. Sienko, Editors

Physical Inorganic Chemistry	*M. J. Sienko and R. A. Plane (Cornell)*
Boron Hydrides	*W. N. Lipscomb (Harvard)*
Metal Ions in Aqueous Solution	*J. P. Hunt (Washington State)*
Inorganic Chemistry of Nitrogen	*W. L. Jolly (Berkeley)*
Inorganic Reaction Mechanisms	*J. O. Edwards (Brown)*

METAL IONS IN AQUEOUS SOLUTION

JOHN P. HUNT
Washington State

W. A. BENJAMIN, INC.
1963 New York Amsterdam

METAL IONS IN AQUEOUS SOLUTION

Library of Congress Catalog Card Number 63-19977
Manufactured in the United States of America

This manuscript was received on December 14, 1962, and the volume was published on September 20, 1963

The publisher is pleased to acknowledge the assistance of Galen Fleck, who edited the manuscript, Cecilia Duray-Bito, who produced the illustrations, and William Prokos, who designed the cover and dust jacket

W. A. BENJAMIN, INC.
2465 Broadway, New York 25, New York

Editors' Foreword

In recent years few fields of chemistry have expanded at a rate to match that of inorganic chemistry. Aside from the stimulus afforded by the demand for new materials, a primary cause for the resurgence has been the application of physics and physical chemistry concepts to inorganic problems. As a result, both researchers active in the field and students entering the field need to become as thoroughly familiar with physical concepts as with descriptive information. However, there is presently no single point of view sufficiently general to organize the entire discipline. Instead, various points of view have arisen corresponding to the most powerful methods of attack in each research area. The synthesis of these different points of view constitutes the present series of monographs. Each monograph is contributed by an inorganic chemist active in a particular research area and reflects the methods of approach characteristic to that area. The operational procedure has been to invite able scientists to write where their interests lead them.

The series fulfills several functions. Through flexible selection of several of the monographs to supplement the introductory volume, it can be used as a textbook for an advanced inorganic chemistry course that makes full use of physical chemistry prerequisites. As a series in total, it is a reference treatise of inorganic chemistry systematized by physical principles. Finally, each monograph by itself represents a specialist's introduction to a specific research field.

It is hoped that the authors contributing to this series have succeeded in directing attention to unsolved problems and that their efforts will be repaid by continued research advances in inorganic chemistry.

M. J. SIENKO
R. A. PLANE

Ithaca, New York
February 1963

Preface

The inorganic chemistry of aqueous solutions has been one of the most exciting fields to develop since the second world war. In particular, the study of metal ion complexes with regard to both equilibrium and kinetic aspects has been very fruitful. New experimental methods involving, for example, the use of isotopes and various electronic equipment promise to make possible the study of the basic phenomena in these areas. The development of ligand field theory has provided new hope of understanding the subtle and complex problems that are involved. Many difficulties remain to be overcome, and future research promises to be rewarding for those with curiosity and skill.

This book is intended to be an introduction to the inorganic chemical research being done with aqueous solution. The treatment is based on lectures given by the author during the past several years to undergraduate seniors and first-year graduate students in chemistry. It is assumed that the reader has a sound background in elementary physical chemistry. Research workers who wish a review of the field will also find this discussion helpful.

No attempt has been made to cover or even mention all the possible subjects in such a large field, but rather to try to introduce the main ideas and results in some areas, and to suggest problems in need of further research. The author believes very strongly in the value of having students read the original literature, and, for this reason, the references given will often be essential to an understanding of a particular topic. Explanations are frequently not provided in the greatest possible detail in the hope that the student will wish to exercise his own mind.

In general, a critical attitude has been adopted, although all sides of all questions are not presented. It is hoped that more than just the author's prejudices are described.

The author's debt to his teachers and colleagues can perhaps best be acknowledged by pointing to the many references cited in this work.

JOHN P. HUNT

Pullman, Washington
March 1963

Contents

1

Gaseous and Aqueous Ions

The gaseous state of matter has been treated theoretically in more detail than any other state and often serves as a reference for trying to understand the more complicated states. For example, the quantum theory of matter is most successful when treating gaseous atoms and molecules, and most of our quantitative and qualitative concepts of chemical binding apply strictly to the gaseous phase. It will be useful to try to relate the chemical properties of aqueous ions to the properties of the analogous gaseous ions (often hypothetical), particularly when we are concerned with thermodynamic processes. We shall want to consider in some detail the reaction between a gaseous ion and water to give a hydrated ion in aqueous solution (hydration). For these reasons, a brief mention of some of the properties of gaseous ions may be worthwhile at this point.

• 1-1 Gaseous Ions

Since we are primarily considering metal ions in this discussion, we can focus our attention on the simplest gaseous cations, that is, those formed from the neutral atoms by loss of electrons. Some briefer comments regarding simple anions and more complex ions that contain two or more bonded atoms will also be in order.

No neutral atom spontaneously loses electrons to form a positive ion. Energy must be supplied, and the process is thus an endothermic one. The ionization can be accomplished by means of collisions of the atom with particles or photons of sufficient energy or by applying a large enough electric field. The term *ionization potential* refers to the energy required to remove an electron from a gaseous species to infinite distance. Values of the ionization potential (IP) can be measured for

Table 1-1 *Ionization potentials of some of the elements*

	Ionization potentials, ev			
Element	First	Second	Third	Fourth
H	13.595			
He	24.580	54.403		
Li	5.390	75.619	122.420	
Be	9.320	18.206	153.850	217.657
F	17.418	34.98	62.65	87.23
Ne	21.559	41.07	64	97
Na	5.138	47.29	71.65	98.88
Mg	7.644	15.03	80.12	109.29
Al	5.984	18.823	28.44	119.96
Cl	13.01	23.80	39.90	53.5
K	4.339	31.81	46	61
Ca	6.111	11.87	51.21	67
Sc	6.56	12.80	24.75	73.9
Ti	6.83	13.57	28.14	43.24
V	6.74	14.65	29.7	48
Cr	6.76	16.5	(31)*	(50)
Mn	7.43	15.6	(32)	(52)
Fe	7.90	16.18		
Co	7.86	17.05		
Ni	7.633	18.15		
Cu	7.724	20.29	29.5	
Zn	9.391	17.96	40.0	
Ga	6.00	20.51	30.6	63.8

* Values in parentheses are uncertain.

successive loss of electrons; the first IP involves loss of an electron to form the monopositive ion, etc.

Some typical IP values[1, 2] in units of electron volts (ev) are given in Table 1-1. (1 ev corresponds to ca. 23 kcal mole^{-1}.) We see that the energies are large; in fact, they are larger than those involved in most ordinary chemical reactions. For a particular atom the successive IP's become larger, and a striking increase is found after an inert-gas type of electronic structure has been formed. The latter increase explains why a maximum charge is found for ions of a given element. Comparisons between different atoms require consideration of sizes, nuclear charges, types of energy level involved (*S*, *P*, *D*, *F*), screening effects of electrons, and other factors. We shall not discuss these factors here, since we are mainly concerned with the properties of the ions after they are formed.

One can formally categorize the types of positive ions formed from the atoms as shown in Table 1-2. The electron clouds of the ions are spherically symmetrical on the time average except for those having incomplete *p* or *d* levels. (Half-filled levels also give rise to spherical symmetry.)

The electron density of a free gaseous ion falls off gradually with increasing distance from the nucleus and reaches zero at infinite distance. Because of this, no theoretical "size" can be assigned to such an ion, although one might arbitrarily take the radius to be the distance such that 90% (or some other value) of the electronic charge is contained within it. Owing to a lack of detailed wave functions for ions, the latter procedure is not a practical one.

Table 1-2 *Electron configurations of cations*

Electron arrangement	Examples
No electrons (nuclei)	H^+, He^{++}
Two electrons (He-like)	Li^+, Be^{++}
Eight electrons in outer shell (Ne- or Ar-like)	Na^+, Mg^{++}, Al^{3+}, K^+
Eighteen electrons in outer shell	Rb^+, Sr^{++}, Y^{3+}, Ga^{3+}
Inert-pair structures or $(n-1)d^{10}ns^2$ structures	In^+, Sn^{++}, Tl^+, Pb^{++}
Transition-metal ions	V^{3+}, Cr^{3+}, Fe^{3+}, Cu^{++}

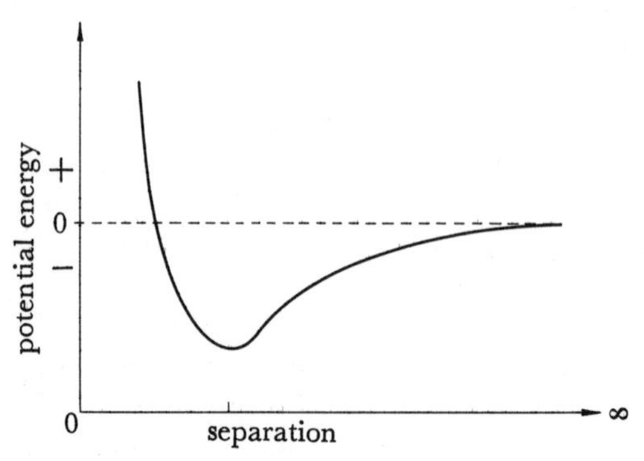

Figure 1-1 *Potential-energy curve for the interaction of two oppositely charged ions.*

An experimental approach might involve studying the collision diameters by using the kinetic theory of gases. This approach also has found little chemical use. The concept of ionic size becomes clearer when one considers the interaction of two oppositely charged ions. At large separations there will be an attraction that increases as the separation decreases. Repulsion due to the electron clouds of the ions also becomes increasingly important as the separation decreases, and at some distance of separation the opposing forces balance. At still smaller separations the repulsions will predominate.

The situation can be represented approximately by the potential-energy curve in Fig. 1-1. The result is that a definite internuclear distance is found for the combination of the ions. One way to represent this situation is to regard the ions as impenetrable, charged spheres of fixed radius, and in this way a pictorial concept of ion size arises. The sums of such radii might be measured experimentally, and then some arbitrary division might be made. Unfortunately, such data are not generally available for gaseous ionic molecules, so that crystalline ionic solids are used for the measurements instead.

The situation in a crystal is quite different, of course, from what would be found for a gaseous pair of ions; but when a gaseous metal ion is surrounded by several ions or molecules (a complex ion, for example), similarities appear. An important difference that remains is that in the gaseous case the interactions between neighboring ions or molecules are essentially absent. One might hope, however, that the relative sizes estimated from crystal data would still be approximately correct. As with all such concepts, the test lies in the success obtained in accounting for other experimental data. At the very least, the sizes obtained from crystal data have proved to be of use in qualitative understanding of ion reactions.

Several investigators have proposed sets of values to be assigned to the ions. The set of *crystal radii* given by Pauling [3] has had considerable use, and we shall use those values in our discussion. A major criterion used in assigning values to the ions is that their sums should correctly give the observed internuclear distances in the crystal. Some typical values are given in Table 2-1. A review of work on ionic sizes has been given by Stern and Amis.[4]

The effective charge on the ion is usually taken to be the formal one based on the difference between the number of protons in the nucleus and the number of electrons present. Modifications of this idea include consideration of the screening effects of inner electrons. For example, ions of the 18-electron type are said to have greater effective charges than the formal charges calculated as above, and that is due to the relatively poorer screening abilities of *d* electrons compared to *s* and *p* electrons. The situation is also more complex in the case of the transition-metal ions, where effects resulting from the nonspherical nature of the ions can be important. These effects will be considered later when use is made of the concept of the size of the ion in considering interaction of the ion with other species, particularly in the hydration process.

Addition of electrons to a neutral atom leads to anions that may form with release or absorption of energy. Because of experimental difficulties, relatively few accurate values for the electron affinities are known. [Electron affinity measures the energy released when an electron is brought from infinite distance and added to the gaseous atom (or ion)]. Some electron affinity values [5, 6] are given in Table 1-3. One notes that the energies released are rather smaller than the ionization potentials of atoms, so that electrons would not spontaneously be transferred from one atom to another unless some other forces were involved. The formation of gaseous halide ions involves about the same amount of energy for all. It is also interesting that the formation of $O^{=}$ is an endothermic process even though an inert-gas electronic structure is achieved.

As in the case of cations, there are problems in describing sizes

Table 1-3 *Electron affinities, in electron volts, of some elements*

Element	Electron affinity, ev
F	3.5
Cl	3.7
Br	3.5
I	3.2
O	1.0 (−7 for 2 electrons added)

and charges of anions. Sizes and charges are generally described in the same way for both cations and anions. Simple anions with inert-gas electronic structures have spherical symmetry of the electron density.

We shall also want to deal with gaseous ions of a more complex nature (ion-molecules), such as $Co(NH_3)_6^{3+}$ and ClO_4^- ions. Much less information is available on the detailed nature of such gaseous ions. From a quantum-mechanical point of view the problems become, in general, those of polyatomic molecules, which cannot be treated quantitatively with much accuracy. Many ions of this type will not be spherically symmetrical, a fact that makes size and charge considerations difficult to deal with. Direct determinations of the molecular geometry are rare because of the difficulty (or impossibility) of obtaining appreciable numbers of the ions in the gaseous state. In general, we have to rely mainly on our theoretical predictions concerning the properties of such ions. Further discussion of the complex ions will be deferred to a later section in which some specific cases are treated.

• 1-2 Aqueous Ions

The existence of ions in aqueous solution appears to have been first postulated in the 1800s to explain the phenomena of electrolysis. In particular, the name of Svante Arrhenius is associated with the foundations of modern ideas about electrolytes. Much argument and discussion have occurred since 1887, when Arrhenius's theory regarding the extent to which substances dissociate into ions was put forth in rather complete form. The problem is complicated in most cases by the absence of direct evidence. It is very difficult theoretically to arrive at criteria for the extent of dissociation, and some arbitrary decisions appear to be necessary.

Without going into detail about these problems, some of the current general ideas can be summarized as follows: In dilute solutions (let us say, arbitrarily, less than 10^{-3} M), strong electrolytes are essentially completely dissociated into ions. These ions are surrounded by solvent molecules and ions of opposite charge. If one adopts the properties of the "infinitely dilute" solution as a reference for ideal behavior for electrolyte solutions, then deviations from such behavior can be discussed in terms of activity coefficients.

In dilute solutions, the theory of Debye and Hückel[7] can be applied. As the solution becomes more concentrated, more elaborate explanations are required; and these, in general, are not entirely satisfactory for quantitative understanding. Among the factors that must be considered are the nature of the solvated ions, the possibility of specific interactions between ions of opposite charge, and the effects of the ions on the properties of the solvent.

Weak electrolytes are incompletely dissociated even in dilute solution. The ions derived from such electrolytes, however, behave as do ions derived from strong electrolytes.

Although positive or negative ions can have a separate existence in the gas phase, in solution the total number of positive charges is always equal to the total number of negative charges simultaneously present. This makes it very difficult to assess the properties of individual ions in solution, since one is always dealing with a mixture.

The equilibrium properties of electrolyte solutions can be treated formally by the methods of classical thermodynamics without reference to the existence of ions or other detailed ideas concerning the nature of the solutions. The thermodynamic data provide the results to be used in testing theories based on various models of the solutions (which may involve the ideas of quantum and statistical mechanics). Ideas concerning the properties of individual aqueous ions come from non-equilibrium phenomena such as ion transport and from the theoretical models.

The concept of ions is usually introduced into the thermodynamic treatment because of a desire to make use of the additional information about the solutions obtained in the other ways. It is not possible, however, to assign thermodynamic properties to individual ions without further nonthermodynamic assumptions. Such assignments cannot be checked directly by using thermodynamic data, and they vary with the theoretical approach.

The situation is similar to that found in assigning electrode potentials to half-reactions or radii to individual ions. The sums of the individual ion properties in a solution can be compared with the thermodynamic data. We shall consider this matter further when discussing certain specific thermodynamic functions of ions. It is convenient for many purposes to try to assign individual ion properties, and we shall do so while keeping in mind the limitations discussed above.

Direct determination of the charge on an aqueous ion presents considerable difficulties. In principle, a fairly direct determination for an ion could be made by electrochemical and diffusion studies. The sign of the charge can be found from the direction of migration of the species in an electric field. Magnitudes for charges could be obtained from the relation

$$D_i = \frac{RT\mu_i}{Z_i\mathfrak{F}}$$

where D_i = ion diffusion coefficient
T = absolute temperature
R = gas constant
μ_i = ion mobility
Z_i = ion charge
$\mathfrak{F}$ = the Faraday [8]

The main use of the above relation is in calculating diffusion coefficients from the other factors. Self-diffusion coefficients can be measured, and, in principle, charges could then be calculated. Very little use appears to have been made of this approach. Strickland [9] has proposed a method of comparing ion charges by using ion-exchange resins, which would give relative values. Our ideas about the charges on ions from simple salts arise mainly from the large body of data concerning electrochemical properties plus analogy with ionic crystals and theoretical predictions of valence theory.

So large an amount of information is consistent with the usual charge assignments that few if any questions are raised about them at the present time. If the charges on associating species are known, then stoichiometry suffices to fix the charge on complex species formed. The question of how the charge is distributed on even simple aqueous ions is less well agreed upon than is the total value. We shall suggest later, for example, that many aqueous cations exist as complex hydrated species such as $Cr(H_2O)_6^{3+}$. It seems likely that the positive charge is distributed among the hydrogen atoms that form the outermost part of the complex. Pauling [10] has made rather specific proposals in this regard as part of his electroneutrality principle. Similar problems arise in assigning charge distributions in ions such as $Cr(CN)_6^{3-}$, $Co(NH_3)_6^{3+}$, and ClO_4^-.

The question of ionic sizes in solution has received much attention. Stern and Amis [4] consider a number of methods under the headings Equilibrium Methods, Kinetic Methods, and The Radii of Ions and Ion-Complexes Determined from Considerations of Chemical Kinetics. The general results of various types of measurement vary considerably among themselves, as might be expected since the different methods measure different aspects of the problem. Since the ions are hydrated in water, the apparent size will depend on, among other things, the number of water molecules assigned to each ion. The hydration numbers themselves are not unambiguously defined, so that the sizes are also in doubt. It appears that no single value that is useful for all properties that can be measured can be assigned to an ion and that one must use values suited to the specific purpose in mind. We shall have occasion to refer to this problem again in later chapters.

References

1. C. E. Moore, "Atomic Energy Levels," *Natl. Bur. Std.* (*U.S.*), **Circ. 467,** 1949.
2. J. Sherman, *Chem. Rev.*, **11,** 93 (1932).
3. L. Pauling, *The Nature of the Chemical Bond*, 3d ed., Cornell University Press, Ithaca, N.Y., 1960, p. 514.
4. K. H. Stern and E. S. Amis, *Chem. Rev.*, **59,** 1–64 (1959).
5. D. Cubicciotti, *J. Chem. Phys.*, **34,** 2189 (1961).
6. D. F. C. Morris and H. N. Schmeising, *Nature*, **181,** 469 (1958).
7. P. Debye and E. Hückel, *Physik. Z.*, **24,** 185 (1923).
8. A. C. Wahl and N. A. Bonner, *Radioactivity Applied to Chemistry*, Wiley, N.Y., 1951, p. 174.
9. J. D. H. Strickland, *Nature*, **169,** 620 (1952).
10. L. Pauling, *The Nature of the Chemical Bond*, 3d ed., Cornell University Press, Ithaca, N.Y., 1960, p. 172.

2

Thermodynamics of Ion Hydration

In this chapter the experimental results for the thermodynamic process involving the transfer of gaseous ions to aqueous solution (hydration) will be considered in some detail. In the following chapter a discussion of these results in terms of theories concerning the nature of the solutions will be given.

• 2-1 Terms and Conventions

We shall be concerned with properties at constant temperature and pressure, and we shall use the Gibbs free energy function F and the entropy S and enthalpy H functions for our discussion of thermodynamic behavior. The sign conventions are that a minus value for ΔF means that the reaction proceeds in the direction written, a minus value for ΔH means that the process as written is exothermic, and a minus value for ΔS means that a decrease in entropy occurs in the process as written.

The symbols themselves will be given no sign when used to represent a conventionally defined process, but they will be given a negative sign for the reverse of such a process. Thus, the heat of formation of a substance from the elements is designated by ΔH_f, whereas the decomposition of the substance into the elements is designated by $-\Delta H_f$. It is always necessary to be careful to take into account these conventions in order to avoid confusion over sign. The units used are kilocalories per mole for ΔF and ΔH and calories per mole per degree (entropy units) for ΔS.

It will also be necessary to make some decisions regarding the standard states to be used for comparison values. Standard states are arbitrary; they are usually chosen on the basis of convenience of use for a particular problem. The reader is referred to a brief discussion of such choices in the book of Robinson and Stokes.[1]

In this book we shall use the following standard states unless otherwise specified. For a gas we shall use the ideal gas at 1 atm pressure at 25 °C; for a solid we shall take the activity (a) to be unity for the stable crystalline form at 25 °C; for a solute we shall use the hypothetical 1-molal (m) concentration also at 25 °C. The latter standard state corresponds to the activity of the solute taken as unity and to a hypothetical solution in which the solute behaves ideally at all concentrations. It is not a solution at infinite dilution, although the partial molal heat content and partial molal heat capacity of the solute have the same value in this standard state as at infinite dilution.

The thermodynamic quantities referred to above, when used for processes occurring with all substances in their standard states, will be designated by the superscript °, as, for example, $\Delta H°$. The symbols (g), (s), and (aq) respectively indicate the gaseous, solid, and aqueous solution states.

• 2-2 Hydration Enthalpy

In order to obtain values for the enthalpy of the hydration process, use is made of the concept of the thermodynamic cycle. Let us use as an example the calculation of the hydration enthalpy for $Na^+(g)$ and $Cl^-(g)$. We can write the following equations:

$$Na^+(g) + Cl^-(g) \rightarrow NaCl(s) \qquad \Delta H_1^\circ \qquad (1)$$

$$NaCl(s) \rightarrow Na^+(aq) + Cl^-(aq) \qquad \Delta H_2^\circ \qquad (2)$$

The sum of (1) and (2) gives the desired process:

$$Na^+(g) + Cl^-(g) \rightarrow Na^+(aq) + Cl^-(aq) \qquad \Delta H_h^\circ \qquad (3)$$

and

$$\Delta H_h^\circ = \Delta H^\circ \text{ hydration} = \Delta H_1^\circ + \Delta H_2^\circ$$

A value for ΔH_1° can be found from theoretical calculations or from thermodynamic data. The theoretical calculations make use of the Born-Mayer approach to the crystal lattice energy, but experimentally one uses the Born-Haber cycle. A good discussion of these methods is found in the books by Pauling [2] and Sienko and Plane.[3] The result of the Born-Mayer theory is an equation of the form

$$U_0 = \frac{NAe^2z^2}{R_0}\left(1 - \frac{1}{n}\right)$$

where U_0 = lattice energy
N = Avogadro's number
A = Madelung constant for the crystal
e = charge on the electron
z^2 = a factor related to the ion charges
n = a parameter which can be evaluated from compressibility measurements and which is related to the repulsive forces in the crystal

If proper attention is paid to standard states and PV work is included, then $U_0 = -\Delta H_1^\circ$. For NaCl the calculated value for ΔH_1° is ca. -183 kcal mole^{-1}.

The Born-Haber cycle for NaCl can be written as follows:

$$\begin{array}{ccc} NaCl(s) & \xrightarrow{-\Delta H_1^\circ} & Na^+(g) + Cl^-(g) \\ \uparrow \Delta H_f^\circ & & \downarrow -I-E \\ Na(s) + \frac{1}{2}Cl_2(g) & \xleftarrow{-S-\frac{1}{2}D} & Na(g) + Cl(g) \end{array}$$

The sum of all the quantities around the cycle must be zero, giving the result that $\Delta H_1^\circ = \Delta H_f^\circ - I - E - S - \frac{1}{2}D$, where the standard enthalpy changes per mole are represented by ΔH_f° for the formation of the crystal of NaCl from the elements, I for the ionization potential of gaseous Na, E for the electron affinity of the gaseous Cl atom, S for the sublimation of Na metal, and D for the dissociation energy of molecular chlorine. Values for these quantities are tabulated in an NBS Circular.[4] By using experimental data from that source, one obtains $\Delta H_1^\circ = -186$ kcal mole^{-1}. (-183 is calculated theoretically.) The value for ΔH_2° can be obtained from measurements on the heat of solution of NaCl and is found to be $+0.9$ kcal mole^{-1} by using the

NBS data. This gives $\Delta H_h^\circ = -186 + 0.9 = -185$ kcal mole^{-1}. Similar calculations can be made for most other simple salts.

• 2-3 Hydration Entropy

The entropy of hydration is usually obtained in a somewhat different way in that the entropies of the gaseous ions are calculated by using the Sackur-Tetrode equation for monatomic gases. This equation, which is obtained by the methods of statistical mechanics, is

$$S(g) = 2.303R\,[\tfrac{3}{2}\log M + \tfrac{5}{2}\log T - \log P + \log Q_e - 0.5055]$$

where R = gas constant
M = atomic weight
T = absolute temperature
P = pressure, atm
Q_e = electronic multiplicity $(2J + 1)$ for the ground state

Since a cancellation occurs, the log Q_e term may be neglected for our purpose if the number of unpaired electrons in the gaseous ion is the same as in the aqueous ion. In any case, the error introduced if cancellation does not occur is usually small compared to the experimental error in ΔS.

The entropies of the aqueous ions can be obtained from EMF measurements on cells or from solubility studies and the third law of thermodynamics. By using the solubility, for example, one can calculate from the equilibrium constant K_{eq} for $NaCl(s) \rightleftharpoons Na^+(aq) + Cl^-(aq)$ the value

$$\Delta F^\circ = -RT\ln K_{eq} = \Delta H^\circ - T\,\Delta S^\circ$$

From the ΔH° value obtained from the measured heat of solution one then calculates $\Delta S^\circ = (\bar{S}^\circ_{Na^+} + \bar{S}^\circ_{Cl^-}) - S^\circ_{NaCl}$. By use of the third law

$$S^\circ_{NaCl} = \int_0^T C_p\,d\ln T + \sum\frac{Q}{T}$$

where the $\bar{S}$'s are the partial molal entropies of the aqueous ions, Cp is the heat capacity at constant pressure, and $\Sigma Q/T$ represents entropy changes due to any transitions occurring between 0°K and T°K. The sum $\bar{S}^\circ_{Na^+} + \bar{S}^\circ_{Cl^-}$ can then be obtained by difference. The entropy of hydration ΔS_h° for the Na^+ and Cl^- ions is then given by

$$\Delta S_h^\circ = (\bar{S}^\circ_{Na^+} + \bar{S}^\circ_{Cl^-}) - [S^\circ_{Na^+}(g) + S^\circ_{Cl^-}(g)]$$

By using values from the NBS circular [4] for the aqueous entropies plus the calculated gaseous entropies, we have

$$\Delta S_h^\circ = 28 - 72 = -44 \text{ eu}$$

• 2-4 Single-Ion Values

The hydration entropies and enthalpies obtained as outlined in the preceding sections refer to values for the sum of the positive and negative ions. Although a division of the sums has no thermodynamic significance, it is useful to assign values to the individual ions as was done in the case of radii. Various assignments have been made on various theoretical grounds, and, as would be expected,[5-7] they lead to somewhat different results.

It seems unlikely that any one scheme is theoretically vastly superior to another, so that we shall simply adopt the procedure of Latimer, Pitzer, and Slansky.[5] These authors used the Born equation [8] as a guide in assigning individual values. We shall discuss the Born equation and its limitations in more detail in the following chapter; here we shall only indicate how it is used in the present connection. Born's expression for the free energy of hydration of an ion is

$$\Delta F_h = -\frac{Ne^2}{2r}\left(1 - \frac{1}{D}\right)$$

where N = Avogadro's number
e = charge on the ion
r = radius of the ion
D = dielectric constant of the solvent

The entropy of hydration is found by taking the derivative of the free energy with respect to temperature, which gives

$$\Delta S_h = \frac{Ne^2}{2r}\frac{1}{D^2}\frac{dD}{dT}$$

Latimer, Pitzer, and Slansky found empirically that, by adding 0.1 A to the Pauling crystal radii for negative ions and 0.85 A to the same radii for positive ions, approximately straight lines are obtained when differences in ΔF_h° for I^- and Br^-, etc., and Cs^+ and Rb^+, etc. (obtained from differences in sums such as $Na^+ + I^-$ and $Na^+ + Br^-$, for example) are plotted vs. $1/r$. They then divided the total ΔF_h° for $Cs^+ + I^-$ in such a way that both positive and negative ions fell on the same curve when ΔF_h° for the individual ions was plotted vs. $1/r$. An analogous procedure was used in obtaining the ΔS_h° values for the ions.

Latimer has given somewhat revised and more extensive data in a later publication.[9] By using the Born equation, he calculates *effective radii* for the ions and suggests that these give a good estimate of ionic sizes in solution. Some values for the hydration quantities (calculated from data in Ref. 3), along with the crystal radii of Pauling and Latimer's effective radii, are given in Table 2-1.

Although we cannot be certain that the individual ion values have any real significance, the relative values should be useful for comparing properties. It is clear, in any case, that large changes in the thermodynamic properties occur on hydrating the ions. The process is exothermic and is accompanied by a negative entropy change. The enthalpy and entropy effects oppose each other ($\Delta F^\circ = \Delta H^\circ - T\,\Delta S^\circ$), but the $T\,\Delta S^\circ$ term will be only a few per cent of ΔF_h°. For example, for Li^+ $\Delta F_h^\circ = -112$ kcal mole^{-1}, $\Delta H_h^\circ = -121$ kcal mole^{-1}, and $T\,\Delta S_h^\circ = -9$ kcal mole^{-1}. The equilibrium constant for the reaction is thus mainly determined by the enthalpy change. The entropy term, however, is of considerable interest from a theoretical point of view, and we shall explore it in the next chapter. Latimer's treatment implies, of course, that the ΔF_h° and ΔH_h° values should be proportional to Z^2/r, where r is his effective value for the radius. This treatment at least correlates the enthalpy and free-energy data quite well with simple parameters obtained from other sources, although it is certainly not unique in this regard.

The entropy data are often treated in a somewhat different manner. The thermodynamic entropy sums such as $\bar{S}^\circ_{Na^+(aq)} + \bar{S}^\circ_{Cl^-(aq)}$ can be split by further assumptions regarding the entropies of single ions. This is of great convenience for tabulation purposes, as is true of the well-known electrode potentials.

The conventional definition is that $\bar{S}^\circ_{H^+} = 0$. By using this definition, tables of aqueous entropies such as the one of Powell and Latimer[10] can be compiled. Powell and Latimer find that the $\bar{S}^\circ$ values obtained at 25°C can be represented by an empirical equation:

$$\bar{S}^\circ = \frac{3}{2} R \ln M + 37 - \frac{270Z}{r_e^{\,2}}$$

Table 2-1 *Thermodynamic values for the hydration of gaseous ions at 25°C*

Ion	$-\Delta H_h^\circ$, kcal mole^{-1}	$-\Delta S_h^\circ$, eu *	Crystal radius, A	Effective radius, A
H^+	258	26		
Li^+	121	28.4	0.60	1.48
Na^+	95	20.9	0.95	
K^+	75	12.4	1.33	
Rb^+	69	9.6	1.48	
Cs^+	61	8.8	1.69	
Ag^+	112	22	1.26	
Tl^+	77	12	1.40	
Be^{++}	591		0.31	1.18
Mg^{++}	456	64	0.65	1.54
Ca^{++}	377	50	0.99	1.84
Sr^{++}	342	49	1.13	2.00
Ba^{++}	308	38	1.35	2.25
Zn^{++}	485	64	0.74	1.44
Cd^{++}	428	55	0.97	1.62
Hg^{++}	430	43	1.10	
Cr^{++}	440		0.84	
Mn^{++}	438	58	0.80	1.59
Fe^{++}	456	65	0.76	
Co^{++}	490	76	0.74	
Ni^{++}	500	77	0.72	
Cu^{++}	500	62	0.72	
Pb^{++}	350	37	1.20	
Al^{3+}	1109	111	0.50	1.38
Sc^{3+}	940		0.81	
Y^{3+}	860		0.93	
La^{3+}	780	88	1.15	
Ga^{3+}	1115	122	0.62	
In^{3+}	980	102	0.81	1.56
Tl^{3+}	990	150	0.95	
Cr^{3+}	1047		0.69	
Fe^{3+}	1041	110	0.64	1.43
F^-	121	36.1	1.36	1.45
Cl^-	90	23.5	1.81	
Br^-	82	19.8	1.95	
I^-	71	14.3	2.16	
$S^=$	330	31	1.84	2.09

* $\bar{S}^\circ_{H^+} \equiv 0$.

where M = atomic weight
Z = absolute value of charge on the ion (1, 2, . . .)
r_e = effective radius

Here the effective radius of cations is found by adding 2.00 A and that of anions by adding 1.00 A to Pauling's crystal radii.

Various attempts to determine the "absolute" entropies of single ions experimentally have been made. A brief discussion of this problem is given in the book by Bockris.[11] The methods involved are of necessity nonthermodynamic and involve various assumptions. The results listed in Ref. 11 give a value of ca. -5 eu for $\bar{S}^\circ_{H^+}$. Latimer [9] arrives at a value of -2.1 eu based on his fit of ΔF°_h and ΔS°_h data to a Z/r (not Z^2/r) plot.

Laidler [12,13] has argued that one should use the value -5.5 eu for $\bar{S}^\circ_{H^+}$ and finds an empirical equation for ions of the form

$$\bar{S}^\circ_{abs} = \frac{3}{2} R \ln M + 10.2 - 11.6 \frac{Z^2}{r_u}$$

where r_u is now Pauling's univalent radius (Ref. 2, page 511). Scott and Hugus [14] differ with Laidler and suggest the equation for cations

$$\bar{S}^\circ_{abs} = \frac{3}{2} R \ln M + 36.5 - 322 \frac{Z}{r_e^2}$$

where the symbols have the same meanings as in Powell and Latimer's equation except that $\bar{S}^\circ_{abs}$ refers to the $\bar{S}^\circ_{H^+} = -5.5$ eu assumption.

King [15] has pointed out that one cannot really expect a good correlation of entropy values as a simple function of charges and radius and that in fact one does not find one. In view of the uncertainties as to the charge distributions in hydrated ions, the hydration numbers, and radii, it seems that King's observations are pertinent and that perhaps for the time being, at least, one should regard equations for $\bar{S}^\circ$ as being mainly useful for correlating data. From a purely thermodynamic point of view we can do all we need to do by using the hydration sums, which avoids the special assumptions discussed above.

• 2-5 Errors

A careful assessment of the errors in the values tabulated in Table 2-1 is not easily made. The numbers for the ± 1 ions are the most reliable, and uncertainties increase as the charge increases. For the

±1 ions the reliability is probably reasonably well indicated by the number of significant figures given; for the +2 and +3 ions the errors in the enthalpies vary with the particular ion in question, although ±5% might be about the average reliability. The entropies of hydration of the +2 and +3 ions may well be in error by 5 to 10 eu independently of any error in dividing between + and − ions. The enthalpy values are not as sensitive as the entropy values to ionic strength effects.

In all cases for the more highly charged ions, though, questions of hydrolysis and complex formation complicate the obtaining of true standard-state values. Unfortunately, compilations of data are not always critical or up to date. For best results one should consult the original literature and try to assess the errors in the values.

In the following chapter we shall consider experimental evidence regarding the detailed nature of the solutions and some theories regarding this nature. The hydration quantities discussed in this chapter will be of considerable use in the theoretical discussion.

References

1. R. A. Robinson and R. H. Stokes, *Electrolyte Solutions*, Academic, New York, 1955, Chap. 2.
2. L. Pauling, *The Nature of the Chemical Bond*, 3d ed., Cornell University Press, Ithaca, N.Y., 1960, pp. 505–511.
3. M. J. Sienko and R. A. Plane, *Physical Inorganic Chemistry*, Benjamin, New York, 1963.
4. "Selected Values of Chemical Thermodynamic Properties," *Natl. Bur. Std.* (*U.S.*) **Circ. 500,** 1952.
5. W. M. Latimer, K. S. Pitzer, and C. M. Slansky, *J. Chem. Phys.*, **7,** 108 (1939).
6. J. D. Bernal and R. H. Fowler, *J. Chem. Phys.*, **1,** 515 (1933).
7. E. J. W. Verwey, *Rec. Trav. Chim.*, **61,** 127 (1942).
8. M. Born, *Physik. Z.*, **1,** 45 (1920).
9. W. M. Latimer, *J. Chem. Phys.*, **23,** 90 (1955).
10. R. E. Powell and W. M. Latimer, *J. Chem. Phys.*, **19,** 1139 (1951).
11. J. O'M. Bockris, *Modern Aspects of Electrochemistry*, Butterworth, London, 1954.
12. K. J. Laidler, *Can. J. Chem.*, **34,** 1107 (1956).
13. K. J. Laidler, *J. Chem. Phys.*, **27,** 1423 (1957).
14. P. C. Scott and Z. Z. Hugus, *J. Chem. Phys.*, **27,** 1421 (1957).
15. E. L. King, *J. Phys. Chem.*, **63,** 1070 (1959).

3

Structure of Water and Ionic Solutions

We have seen in the preceding chapter that large energy and entropy changes accompany the placing of ions into water. It is of considerable interest to try to understand these changes and other phenomena in terms of the various interactions occurring in the solutions. Let us start with a look at water itself.

• 3-1 Properties of Water

Water is a liquid that is quite unique in its properties. It has, for example, a relatively high boiling point and high heat capacity; it exhibits an expansion on freezing and a maximum density near 4 °C. In a general way these phenomena are explained by saying that water has a highly hydrogen-bonded structure. Before looking into this further, it may be worthwhile to examine the gaseous water molecule briefly.

As is well known, the gaseous H_2O molecule is a bent molecule; the HOH angle being about 105°. This can be understood in terms of approximately sp^3 hybridization of the oxygen orbitals; two of the orbitals being used for bonding with hydrogen atoms and the other two being used to contain lone or unshared pairs of electrons. The

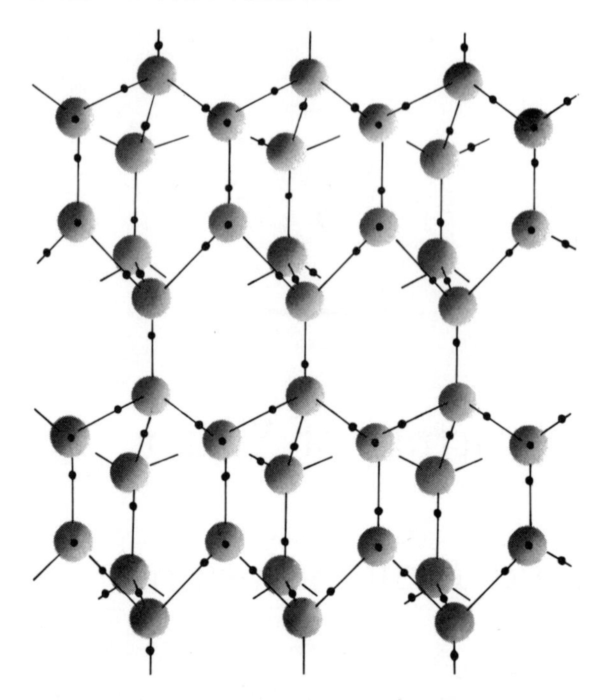

Figure 3-1 ***The arrangement of molecules in the ice crystal.*** [*From L. Pauling, The Nature of the Chemical Bond, 3d ed., Cornell University Press, Ithaca, N.Y.*, 1960, p. 465; *reproduced with permission.*]

repulsions exerted by the lone-pair electrons on the bonding electrons account for the fact that the observed angle is less than the tetrahedral angle (109°28′). These lone pairs can be used in hydrogen bonding and would be expected to aid in forming a tetrahedral structure about the oxygen. The bent structure also explains the fact that the water molecule has a dipole moment (1.87×10^{-18} esu).

X-ray scattering measurements on ordinary ice show a tetrahedral arrangement of oxygen atoms which can be understood in terms of a tetrahedral arrangement of lone pairs and hydrogen atoms about the oxygen atom. The arrangement is shown schematically in Fig. 3-1. The structure is far from being a close-packed one; it rather resembles that of the wurtzite crystal, ZnS. On melting, this structure is presumed to collapse to a more closely packed one, since the density increases. Further collapse occurs on heating until a maximum density is reached; beyond this the increase in kinetic energy causes an expansion and decreasing density.

In liquid water the structure is less clear. The classic experiments of Morgan and Warren [1] (recently confirmed by Brady and Romenow [2]) using X-ray scattering indicate that the tetrahedral arrangement persists in small regions of the liquid, although no long-range order (as in a crystal) is found. The number of nearest neighbors will fluctuate with time, but at 25 °C most of the water molecules will have four close neighbors. The association is due to hydrogen bonds. The small value of the enthalpy of fusion of ice (1.44 kcal $mole^{-1}$) compared to the estimate of 10 kcal $mole^{-1}$ as the contribution of hydrogen bonding to the sublimation enthalpy of ice leads to the conclusion that only a small fraction (ca. 15%) of the hydrogen bonds are broken on melting.

The best description of the detailed arrangement in liquid water is a matter of some dispute. One such description has been given by Bernal and Fowler [3] in terms of a quartz-like structure based on tetrahedra more closely packed than in ice. Pauling [4] has argued against this picture and suggests a clathrate-like structure involving pentagonal dodecahedra arranged in random ways relative to one another. In any case, it now seems clear that liquid water does have a local tetrahedral structure with considerable long-range randomness and with fluctuating arrangements of H_2O molecules. A consequence of this is that water cannot be regarded as a uniform dielectric medium in the presence of ions and that specific effects are expected. Thus the question of how a particular ion affects and accommodates to the water structure will enter into a detailed discussion of the nature of ionic solutions.

Water has a quite high dielectric constant (78 at 25 °C) compared to most liquids, although liquid HF, HCN, formamide, and a few other compounds do have higher values. The relatively high solubility of ionic compounds in water is certainly related to this property. The specific heat of water (ca. 1 cal g^{-1}) is also relatively high and is due to the previously mentioned interactions between water molecules. Very pure water has a specific conductivity of ca. 4×10^{-8} ohm^{-1} cm^{-1} that is due to dissociation into hydrated H^+ and OH^- ions. The ion product $[H^+][OH^-]$ has the value 1×10^{-14} at 25 °C.

Raman and infrared spectral studies have also been made on water. They indicate intermolecular vibrations, although exact interpretation is difficult. The lifetimes of aggregates, of course, can be very short and still give rise to observable spectra, and about all one can say from these observations is that these lifetimes are longer than ca. 10^{-12} sec.

That the lifetimes are short is indicated by the work of Collie, Hasted, and Ritson [5] on the variation of the dielectric constant with frequency. The measured dielectric constant depends to a large extent on the orientation of the water dipoles in an electric field. If sufficiently high frequencies are used, the orientation process cannot follow the variation in the electric field and the observed dielectric constant will decrease at high frequencies. Collie et al. used frequencies of about 10^{10} sec^{-1} and found that the data were well accounted for by orientation of only a single species from 0 to 75°C. This suggests that associated species have very short lifetimes, since otherwise the relative proportions of such species would be expected to vary with temperature and thus show the presence of more than one orienting species over the temperature range.

If gaseous ions are to be placed in water (hydrated), we shall want to investigate the nature of the hydrated ions as well as the changes, if any, caused in the solvent.

• 3-2 Effects of Ions on Water Structure

Studies using X-ray and Raman methods have been made on the effect of ions on the water structure. The general conclusions from such experiments are that the water structure may be still present in ionic solutions although it can be altered in various ways. X-ray work by Brady,[6,7] for example, on concentrated solutions of KOH, KCl, and LiCl showed that in KOH the radial distribution curve was very similar to that of pure water with an enhancement of the water peak. He calculated that there are four molecules of water around each K^+ and six around the OH^-. It appears that the $K(H_2O)_4^+$ species (presumably tetrahedral) can fit into the water structure without altering it very much. The results on KCl solutions indicated a lessening or breakdown of the water structure presumably due to the Cl^- ion. In LiCl the H_2O-H_2O nearest-neighbor peak is absent, again suggesting a breakdown of the water structure. Such results are very interesting, but it must be remembered that they are not necessarily applicable to more dilute solutions.

Schultz and Hornig [8] have done a rather detailed study on the effects of dissolved alkali halides on the Raman spectrum of water.

The results again show only one detectable local structure for water consistent with the dielectric constant measurements mentioned above. The salts LiCl, LiI, KI, CsF, and CsI were used over a range of concentrations up to saturation. Both the H_2O stretching and bending vibrations showed a marked effect due to variation of anions but no cation effect in going from Li^+ to Cs^+. The exact interpretation of these results is not clear, since the ions may be associated in the concentrated solutions used. The authors suggest that hydrogen bonding to the anions and distortion of the water structure are responsible for the anion effects. The absence of a cation effect may be due to ion association in which the cation is shielded by the larger anions. Walrafen [9] has succeeded in studying aqueous selenious acid at concentrations as low as 1.6 *M*, which suggests that the Raman approach may be a very useful one in studying aqueous species.

An interesting aspect of the nature of water has to do with the very high mobilities of H^+ and OH^- ions in water. The value for H^+ is 36.2×10^{-4} cm^2 volt^{-1} sec^{-1} compared to 5.3×10^{-4} cm^2 volt^{-1} sec^{-1} for Na^+. For OH^- the value is 19.8×10^{-4} cm^2 volt^{-1} sec^{-1} compared to 7.9×10^{-4} cm^2 volt^{-1} sec^{-1} for Cl^-. The high mobilities are explained by the rapid proton transfers represented by the equations:

$$H_2O + H_3O^+ \xrightarrow{k_1} H_3O^+ + H_2O \quad (1)$$

$$H_2O + OH^- \xrightarrow{k_2} OH^- + H_2O \quad (2)$$

A good review of this subject is found in the paper of Eigen and DeMaeyer.[10] Meiboom [11] has studied these reactions by using nuclear magnetic resonance (NMR) of protons and O^{17} in water. He finds for k_1 the value $(10.6 \pm 4) \times 10^9$ liter mole^{-1} sec^{-1} and for k_2 the value $(3.8 \pm 1.5) \times 10^9$ liter mole^{-1} sec^{-1}, which is in good agreement with estimates from the mobilities. Therefore, very rapid changes involving proton transfers, in addition to the rapid changes involving interactions between H_2O molecules, occur in water.

• 3-3 Nature of Hydrated Ions

Considerable attention has been given over the years to the question of the nature of the hydrated ions. In particular, attempts have been made to decide whether a definite number of H_2O molecules (the hydration number) is associated with a particular ion giving rise to a molecular species. The answer clearly depends on the criterion used for defining a species. Redlich and Hood [12] have emphasized the need for an experimental criterion and believe that Raman spectroscopy provides the best one. The basic idea is that an aggregate should persist long enough to permit the observation of vibrational spectra (ca. 10^{-12} sec). Such a criterion is, of course, arbitrary, but it seems to be a reasonable one and we shall use it in our discussion.

Bockris [13] has reviewed the older experimental data on the determination of hydration numbers. An examination of the data shows a great variability in the results depending on the method used. The variation can be understood in terms of a simple model in which one considers that an ion exerts an influence on H_2O molecules over some distance from the ion. The nearest H_2O molecules will be most affected, and the interaction will become weaker for more distant ones. The nearest H_2O molecules may in fact be joined by bonds in the usual chemical sense, and species as defined by Redlich then exist. These near molecules are often said to make up the first or inner *coordination sphere* of the hydrated ion. The term "sphere" arises because of the roughly spherical symmetry such an aggregate would have. This unit is also surrounded by H_2O molecules, interacting less strongly, that make up the outer coordination spheres. At some distance from the ion the H_2O molecules are essentially under the same influences as in pure water. The support for such a model comes from experimental and theoretical considerations. We shall first consider the experimental evidence.

We have already referred to X-ray work on very concentrated solutions in which hydration numbers were determined for some ions. It has been known for some time, of course, that many salt hydrates contain hydrated ions in the crystal, and thus it is not surprising to find evidence for them in concentrated solutions. Work in this area is of considerable importance as a guide to understanding solutions at all concentrations. Methods that can be used in much more dilute solutions are particularly needed.

In the case of the ion $Cr(H_2O)_6{}^{3+}$ rather direct evidence for the species in much less concentrated solutions than used in the X-ray work has come from O^{18}-exchange experiments.[14] The exchange reaction can be formulated as follows:

$$Cr(H_2O)_X{}^{3+} + XH_2O^{18} \rightleftharpoons Cr(H_2O^{18})_X{}^{3+} + XH_2O$$

where X is to be determined. The exchange could be followed by sampling the solvent by means of distillations. It was found that the half-time for isotopic exchange was about 40 hr at 25°C; thus, a very slow reaction is involved. It was then possible to determine the number of slowly exchanging water molecules attached to the Cr^{3+} by observing the amount of isotope dilution immediately after mixing a Cr^{3+} solution with H_2O^{18}. Not all of the water in the Cr^{3+} solution is immediately available to mix with and thus dilute the H_2O^{18}. The number of "unbound" H_2O molecules was calculated from the observed isotopic dilution, and by subtracting this number from the total present the number of "bound" waters was found. The ratio of molecules of bound H_2O to ions of Cr^{3+} was then found to be 6. Chromium concentrations were about 1 to 3 *M*. These results set a lower limit, at least, for the hydration number.

The large body of data on Cr(III) coordination compounds in which chromium has a characteristic coordination number of 6 makes it rather certain that the true first-sphere hydration number has been measured. Since the long half-time for exchange is also quite in line with the kinetic properties of Cr(III) complexes in general, it becomes clear that the $Cr(H_2O)_6{}^{3+}$ species is as much a real species as the more familiar ones such as $Cr(NH_3)_6{}^{3+}$ and $Cr(NCS)_6{}^{3-}$ or, for that matter, $NO_3{}^-$, which also shows a slow O^{18} exchange. Such an approach as described above requires that the exchange rate be measurable, which unfortunately limits the applicability of the method. An extension of the method to a faster exchange reaction has been made for Al^{3+}.[15] By using a flow technique permitting determination of half-lives as low as 10^{-2} sec, the hydration number for Al^{3+} was found to be 6 also.

A more subtle approach by Feder and Taube using O^{18}-isotope effects also gives support to the idea of a first-sphere hydration number, although hydration numbers are not obtained.[16] If one distills a fraction of a sample of pure water containing the usual abundance of O^{18} (ca. 0.2 atom %), one finds that the ratio H_2O^{16}/H_2O^{18} is greater for the distillate than for the water originally. This general effect is referred to as an isotope fractionation. If $Cr(H_2O)_6{}^{3+}$ is added to ordinary water and a sample distilled *at once*, the ratio found is the same as for the pure water (ca. 1.005). If, however, the exchange reaction is allowed to go to completion (reach equilibrium) and a sample is then distilled, the ratio is larger (ca. 1.010). It is found that the O^{18} has concentrated slightly in the $Cr(H_2O)_6{}^{3+}$ species and thus has reduced the amount of O^{18} present in the solvent H_2O.

Since the effect is found only after exchange has occurred, it is produced in the first coordination sphere. From the theory of isotope effects this means that the vibrational frequencies of $Cr—O^{16}$ and $Cr—O^{18}$ are different and implies a long enough lifetime for vibrations to occur. Thus the observation of a similar effect in other cases would suggest very strongly the existence of a similar hydrated species. (Although no one would probably expect things to be otherwise, the result also would show that it is the O of the H_2O molecule that is attached to the ion.) Such a criterion is essentially the same as that of Redlich.

Similar effects are found for a number of positive ions, but not for all. One might expect that anions would also give an effect; but if they do so, it is too small to measure by the techniques used. Among the cations which show evidence for the first-sphere hydration are Al^{3+}, Mg^{++}, Li^+, H^+, and Ag^+. Na^+, K^+, NH_4^+, and Cs^+ do not produce the effect discussed above. A detailed examination of the data obtained [17] also indicates that the larger ions such as Cs^+ cause some reduction in the partially ordered structure of water.

NMR studies using O^{17} have also shed light on the hydration question. A preliminary study [18] has shown that a separate NMR peak due to the hydrated ion can be observed for Be^{++}, Al^{3+}, and Ga^{3+}. In principle, hydration numbers might be found by a refinement of the technique. The observation of a peak due to the hydrated ion requires that the lifetime of the species be ca. 10^{-4} sec or longer. Connick and co-workers [19–22] have used NMR line-broadening techniques on H_2O^{17} to measure the exchange rates of water between hydrated ions and solvent. Their work gives mean lifetimes for the hydrated species as follows: Fe^{3+}, ca. 10^{-4} sec; Mn^{++}, ca. 10^{-7} sec; Fe^{++}, ca. 10^{-6} sec; Co^{++}, ca. 10^{-6} sec; Ni^{++}, ca. 10^{-4} sec; Cu^{++}, ca. 10^{-4} for equatorial H_2O and ca. 10^{-8} for axial H_2O. These lifetimes presumably apply to the octahedral $M(H_2O)_6^{+n}$ species except that for Cu^{++} there is indicated a distorted octahedron in which two water molecules are farther away from the Cu^{++} than the other four, the two axial water molecules exchanging much faster than the equatorial ones. Some evidence was also obtained for a tetrahedral $Co(H_2O)_4^{++}$ species near 100°C. These studies do not give direct information on coordination numbers but do suggest them for Co^{++} and Cu^{++}. In any case the results provide good evidence for definite hydrated species in the cases mentioned.

Although not directly concerned with the nature of metal ions, the question of the nature of the hydrated proton is of some interest to our discussion. A gaseous proton would have a very small size compared to the crystal radii we have been using and thus would be expected to show a large interaction with H_2O. Baughan [23] gives a value for ΔH_h° of -283 kcal mole^{-1} for the proton. The proton affinity for gaseous H_2O is ca. -182 kcal mole^{-1}, which leaves -100 kcal mole^{-1} for the reaction $H_3O^+(g) \rightarrow H_3O^+(aq)$. At the present time there is considerable evidence [24,25] that the hydrated species in ordinary concentrations is $H_3O^+(H_2O)_3$, with a central hydronium ion hydrogen-bonded symmetrically to the three H_2O molecules.

The older methods for hydration numbers (see Ref. 13) involve studies on ionic mobilities, compressibilities, dielectric constants, densities, dialysis, and solvent transport in cells, among others. Hydration numbers for Na^+ as high as 700 have been reported. Many of these methods clearly measure effects involving more than the immediate vicinity of the ion, and different methods detect the influence of the ion at different distances.

It appears to be difficult to obtain a clear picture of the nature of the hydration beyond the first sphere from either experimental or theoretical work. Changes in arrangements beyond the first sphere appear to be very rapid, and thus a specific arrangement is hard to detect. We have mentioned in connection with the X-ray and isotope studies that changes in the apparent structure of water seem to be caused by ions, but no direct information on the arrangement of water molecules beyond the first sphere has been obtained. In the discussion to follow we shall describe some (but not all) of the attempts to obtain theoretical models for ionic solutions.

• 3-4 Models for Calculating the Hydration Enthalpy of Ions

The earliest and simplest model for calculation of hydration free energies and entropies is that of Born [26] referred to in the preceding chapter. The ion is considered to be a rigid sphere of radius r and charge q to be placed in a medium of dielectric constant D. The free energy of hydration is calculated as the difference in the reversible electrical work required to charge the sphere in vacuo and in the medium. This difference in work equals the energy released when the charged sphere is placed in solution. From classical electrostatic theory one proceeds to bring a charge dq from ∞ to the surface of a sphere of radius r and charge q (considered to be at the center of the sphere). The charge dq is then raised to q. The total work is then

$$\int_0^q \int_\infty^r \frac{q}{Dr^2}\,dq\,dr = -\frac{q^2}{2Dr}$$

This process is often called the Born charging process. D is 1 in a vacuum, so that

$$\Delta F_h \text{ (per sphere)} = -\frac{q^2}{2r} + \frac{q^2}{2Dr} = -\frac{q^2}{2r}\left(1 - \frac{1}{D}\right)$$

In the general case for N ions of charge Ze the equation becomes

$$\Delta F_h = -\frac{NZ^2e^2}{2r}\left(1 - \frac{1}{D}\right)$$

ΔS_h is then obtained by differentiation with respect to temperature, which gives

$$\Delta S_h = \frac{NZ^2e^2}{2r}\frac{1}{D^2}\frac{\partial D}{\partial T}$$

ΔH_h can be obtained by using the relation $\Delta F = \Delta H - T\,\Delta S$.

One might expect that such a simple model would have difficulties for several reasons. A difficulty common to most models involves the choice of values for r, the ionic size. Poor agreement with the experimental data is found if the crystal radii are used. Latimer, Pitzer, and Slansky,[27] as previously noted, found it necessary to use an effective radius obtained by adding 0.85 A to the crystal radii of cations and 0.10 A to the radii of anions. When this is done for ΔF_h°, values calculated from the Born equation are in quite good agreement with the experimental data. There seems to be no independent way of justifying any set of radius values to be used.

Another difficulty is that the proper value to use for D is not certain. It is expected that D near an ion will have a smaller value than for pure water. The calculated free energy values, however, are not very sensitive to the value of D if it is large compared to 1. No mention is made in such a model of either hydrated species or the structure of water, both of which factors would be expected to be important.

The entropy values are much more sensitive to the value for D and its temperature coefficient. Latimer's approach,[28] and to some extent that of King,[29] leads to a dependence of ΔS_h on Z rather than Z^2. If the Born equation as used by Latimer is to be correct, then $\partial D/\partial T$ must depend on Z. Latimer has suggested that this may be the case, but again there seems to be no independent evidence for this idea. Although this model gives no detailed insight into the nature of the ionic solutions, it is a useful one for correlating data and getting approximate values for the thermodynamic quantities in aqueous solutions.

Noyes [30] has taken an approach different to the use of the Born equation in that he considers the ion sizes to be known but allows for variation of the solvent dielectric constant as a function of distance from the ion. His discussion is thorough and informative, in addition to providing many useful data. Although Latimer's work predicts that ions of the same *effective* radius will have the same thermodynamic hydration parameters regardless of the sign of the charge, Noyes' results lead to the conclusion that anions have larger (more negative) values of ΔF°_h, ΔH°_h, and ΔS°_h than cations of the same *ionic* radius and charge magnitude. This "asymmetry effect" will be mentioned again in discussing more detailed models.

The classic structural approach to ion hydration and the structure of H_2O was made by Bernal and Fowler (B-F).[3] Although a number of objections can be raised to their treatment, their ideas have greatly influenced later workers and it seems worthwhile to briefly consider their method here. These authors consider H_2O to have a structure based on a tetrahedral arrangement of H_2O molecules as indicated by the X-ray work. They then consider the hydration energy of an ion as arising from four factors:

1. The ion is coordinated to a definite number of H_2O molecules in the first coordination sphere, forming, in a sense, bonds with the molecules and releasing energy.

2. The hydrated ion formed in (1) interacts with close H_2O molecules, which have different arrangements than in the bulk H_2O. Energy will also be released in this process.

3. The hydrated ion interacts with more distant molecules of H_2O having essentially the properties of bulk water, again releasing energy.

4. Rearrangements in the structure of water will take place, which will lead to an absorption of energy.

There are considerable difficulties in making quantitative estimates of these four factors. Factor 2, in fact, is not directly included

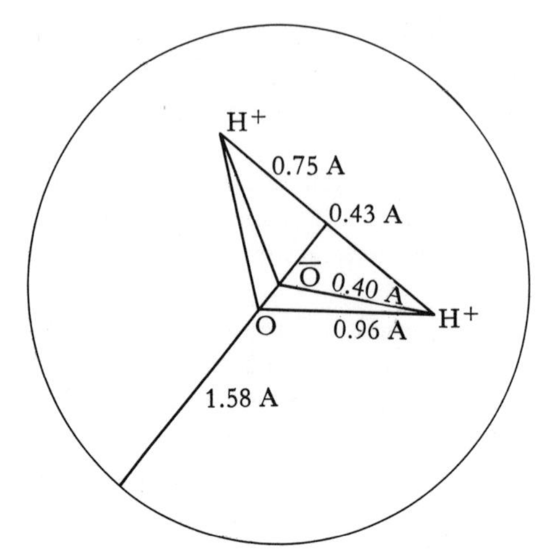

Figure 3-2 *The water molecule model.* H+, H+ *are the hydrogen nuclei;* O *is the oxygen nucleus; and* Ō *is the center of the negative charge.* [*From J. D. Bernal and R. H. Fowler, J. Chem. Phys.,* **1**, 528 (1933); *reproduced with permission.*]

in the calculations. The problem of assigning a value to the radius of the ion is, as always, present. Here the ionic radius (Goldschmidt) and a radius of 1.38 A for the H_2O molecule are used in the computations. The energy of interaction in the first sphere is calculated by using a dipole model for water as shown in Fig. 3-2. The orientations taken for H_2O coordinated to the ions are shown in Fig. 3-3. Even with this simple model it is difficult to estimate all the energy terms involved, and only an approximate value is obtained. Factors 2 and 3 are essentially lumped together, and the energy is calculated by using the Born expression with an empirically determined effective radius (larger than the ionic radius). Presumably, the use of the bulk dielectric constant is justified, since the ionic charge is spread out more and will have less effect on the water. For the fourth term a rather involved argument is needed to obtain a value for the reorientation energy, but it is again based on the dipole model for H_2O and the tetrahedral structure of the liquid.

In spite of all the assumptions involved, the calculated values agree fairly well with the experimental values obtained by Bernal and Fowler by dividing the heat of hydration of K^+ and F^- ions approximately equally. A check of the B-F calculations for the *sums* ($n Cl^- + M^{n+}$) against Latimer's values also shows quite good agreement, although values for single ions differ because of the different arbitrary divisions made. Although the B-F model is more in accord with ideas concerning the structure of ionic solutions, it is still rather crude and certainly no better than the Born equation as used by Latimer or Noyes as far as quantitative use is concerned.

In view of the nature of the calculations, the apparent agreement of calculated and experimental values must be partly due to the canceling of errors in various terms. An interesting observation made by Bernal and Fowler is that the hydration energy of an ion is approximately equal to the energy released when the electrons are returned to the gaseous ion to form the neutral atom (the negative of the total ionization potential). This suggests that considerable electron transfer occurs in the interaction of the H_2O molecules with the ion. This idea is, of course, embodied in Pauling's electroneutrality principle mentioned in Chap. 1. Bernal and Fowler did not attempt to calculate entropies, and a more complex model is needed for that purpose.

Eley and Evans [31] tried to give a more exact treatment by using a model similar to that of Bernal and Fowler. In order to calculate ΔH_h°, they used a cycle and attempted to evaluate the steps separately. In step 1 a tetrahedral group of five H_2O molecules is removed from the solvent to the gas phase, which leaves a "hole" in the solvent and

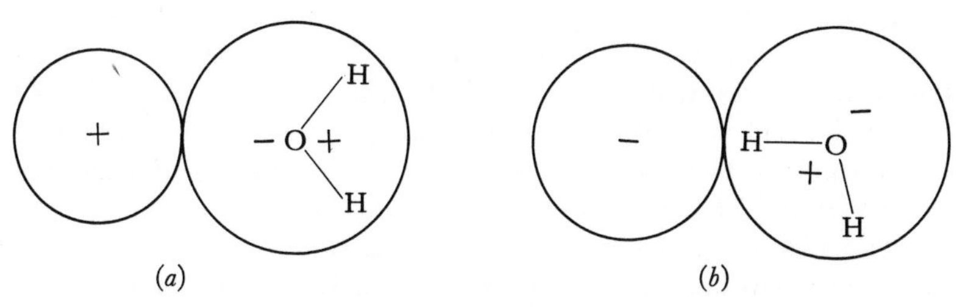

Figure 3-3 *Orientation of water molecules with respect to positive and negative ions. [From J. D. Bernal and R. H. Fowler, J. Chem. Phys.,* **1,** 535 (1933); *reproduced with permission.]*

requires an energy λ. In step 2, the gaseous tetrahedral group is dissociated into five separate H_2O molecules, which requires an energy β. In step 3, four H_2O molecules are coordinated tetrahedrally about univalent ions and six octahedrally about more highly charged metal ions, which releases an energy π. In step 5, the metal ion-H_2O complex of step 4 is returned to the solvent hole, which involves a possible gain or loss of energy γ. In step 6, the remaining gaseous H_2O molecule is returned to the solvent with a release of energy L. Then

$$\Delta H_h^\circ = \lambda + \beta - \pi - \gamma - L$$

The calculations still involve classical ones using a spherical model for H_2O with charges placed in the sphere to reproduce the measured dipole moment. Ionic crystal radii are used for the metal ions. The reader is referred to the original paper for details of the calculation, and here we shall only indicate some of the considerations involved.

The calculation of π neglects the interactions between H_2O molecules in the tetrahedron and assumes that π is 4 (or 6) times the interaction energy of the ion with a single H_2O molecule. Essentially only the coulomb terms $Ze\alpha e/r$, where Z is the ionic charge and α is the charge assigned to H or O, are used. The orientations of H_2O about cations and anions are taken as those of Bernal and Fowler (Fig. 3-3). In principle, one should include effects due to polarization, dispersion forces, and repulsions; but these are assumed negligible here. β is calculated in essentially the same way as π, and the neglect of H_2O-H_2O interactions tends to cancel out between π and β.

The authors try to evaluate $\lambda - \gamma$, which includes consideration of (1) the fact that the hole may not fit the tetrahedral ion-H_2O complex and thus may need to shrink or expand, (2) the H_2O surrounding the ion group may reorient, and (3) the charged group will affect more distant H_2O molecules. Item 3 was accounted for by using the Born equation with $r = (r \text{ ion} + 2r_w)$, where r_w = radius of H_2O, taken to be 1.88 A, and by assuming that $D = 78$ at this distance. Item 1 was neglected because of difficulty in trying to evaluate it accurately and the feeling that only a relatively small energy is involved. The reorientation item 2 was estimated graphically.

For coordination-number-4 ions the results are that β is ca. 21 kcal mole^{-1}, $\lambda - \gamma$ (excluding the Born energy) is ca. 8 kcal mole^{-1} for cations and ca. 20 kcal mole^{-1} for anions, and L is ca. -10 kcal mole^{-1}. This gives the formulas

$$\Delta H_h^\circ(+) = 19 - E_{\mathrm{BC}} - \pi \quad \text{and} \quad \Delta H_h^\circ(-) = 31 - E_{\mathrm{BC}} - \pi$$

where E_{BC} is the Born charging term mentioned above. For six coordinated cations the formula becomes

$$\Delta H_h^\circ = 15 - E_{BC} - \pi$$

Some values for the E_{BC}, π, and ΔH_h° terms are listed in Table 3-1.

The results of these calculations suggest that the interaction of the ion with H_2O appreciably extends beyond the first coordination sphere, especially for +3 ions. A comparison of the calculated values for cation-anion sums with Latimer's experimental data shows in general that the calculated values are too low. This might be expected, since the interaction of the ion and the first sphere of H_2O molecules neglects all forces but the simple coulombic ones. As found by Bernal and Fowler, but not by Latimer or Noyes, the ΔH_h° values are the same for anions and cations of equal *crystal* radii. In the Eley and Evans model this occurs because asymmetry effects between π and $\lambda - \gamma$ are canceled. The ΔH_h° values will not be a simple function of Z^2e^2/r_{cryst} according to this model, which seems to be the case for all detailed models.

Verwey [32] has emphasized the idea that anions and cations of the same crystal radius give rise to different ΔH_h° values (asymmetry effect). He considered the first-sphere interaction in more detail than Eley and Evans and arrived at a different orientation of H_2O near a cation. Verwey also used various models for the H_2O molecule itself and concluded that the asymmetry effect is real.

Buckingham [33] has examined the preceding calculations and concludes that several modifications should be made, including taking into

Table 3-1 *Calculated hydration energies with E_{BC} and π terms*

Ion	E_{BC}	π	$-\Delta H_h^\circ$
F^-	39.8	82.4	91
Cl^-	35.6	54.5	59
Li^+	46.0	105.5	133
Be^{++}	196	379	560
Al^{3+}	441	569	995

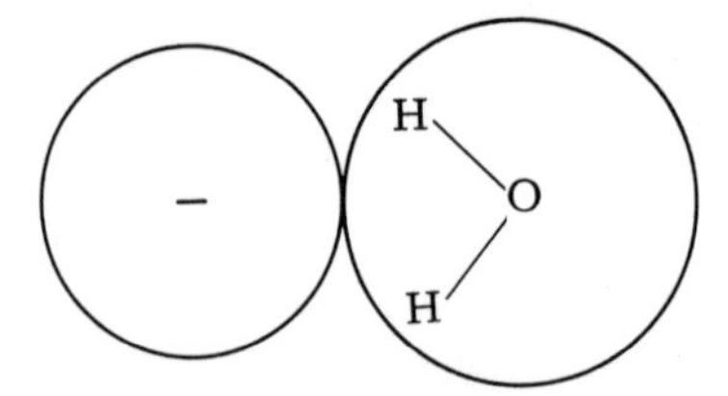

Figure 3-4 *Buckingham's model for the orientation of a water molecule with respect to an anion.*

account the important lone-pair electrons in H_2O, induced multipole moments, London forces, and the effect of the ionic charge on the dielectric constant. In addition, he concludes that the orientation of H_2O about an anion is as shown in Fig. 3-4 rather than the one used by the previously mentioned authors (Fig. 3-3). This seems reasonable in view of the lone-pair electrons on oxygen. In models of this type the repulsive forces are taken into account by using a hard-sphere picture for the ions and H_2O so that distances are fixed by the radii. This procedure can hardly be accurate, but there seems to be little else that can be done at the present. The calculations by Buckingham essentially involve a more detailed calculation of the first-sphere interaction plus using a modified Born equation for the longer-range interactions. His values are calculated only for the $\pm$ ions of the alkali metals and the halogens, assuming coordination number 4, and are high by 10 to 20%. The model used also accounts for the asymmetry effect previously mentioned.

It appears that several similar models lead to fairly good calculated values for heats of hydration, at least for ions of low charge, and that it would be difficult to choose one model as superior on the basis of the agreement with experimental data. All the models have difficulties and involve unknown parameters, so that the agreement found must be to some extent fortuitous. It is clear that refinements might be made in principle in the various calculations, but it is not clear how to make them properly.

A very serious problem is the question of what to use for the ion size. To the extent that the forces in solution resemble those in a crystal, the use of crystal radii seems reasonable, but some differences would be expected nonetheless. The interaction of an ion with the nearest water molecules should be calculated by quantum-mechanical methods, which, however, are not available at this time. Some covalent character is certainly expected in the binding of H_2O to an ion.

A better classical charge model for water might be found eventually, although great improvement here seems unlikely. The question of how many H_2O molecules are in the first coordination sphere is, of course, a crucial one the answer to which is not usually known. The concept of such "primary hydration" has itself been challenged at various times, particularly for large, low-charge ions. Samoilov,[34] for example, has emphasized the idea that ions such as K^+, Cs^+, and I^- do not really form hydrated species with a definite hydration number. This argument depends, of course, on the arbitrary definition one has to take for a species. At the present time, the concept of hydration numbers, at least for most cations, still seems to be a useful if not a necessarily precise one. The long-range interactions can probably be reasonably well handled by using a modified Born equation, although orientation effects remain difficult to assess.

• 3-5 Crystal Field Effects

A complication that enters for transition-metal ions is of some special interest. The crystal field theory was developed to account for deviations of transition-metal ions from the behavior expected for a spherical charge distribution in crystals. Ideas from the theory have been applied to metal-ion interactions in general by various persons. (See, for example, Ref. 3 in Chap. 2.) Orgel[35,36] has suggested that the hydration energies for transition-metal ions should be influenced by the crystal field effects.

A simplified discussion for the first-row transition elements can be given as follows. If one regards the interaction between the metal ion and the H_2O molecules as being a classical ionic one, then the $3d$ electrons of the metal ion do not directly participate in the binding. They will not, however, remain in the same energy states as found for the free ion. This can be understood somewhat naïvely for octahedral six-coordinate ions in terms of repulsion of the $3d$ electrons by the ligand electrons. The conventional representation of the $3d$ orbitals is shown in Fig. 3-5. The $d_{x^2-y^2}$ and d_{z^2} orbitals "point" at the ligands, and the d_{xy}, d_{xz}, and d_{yz} orbitals point between ligands. The effect of the

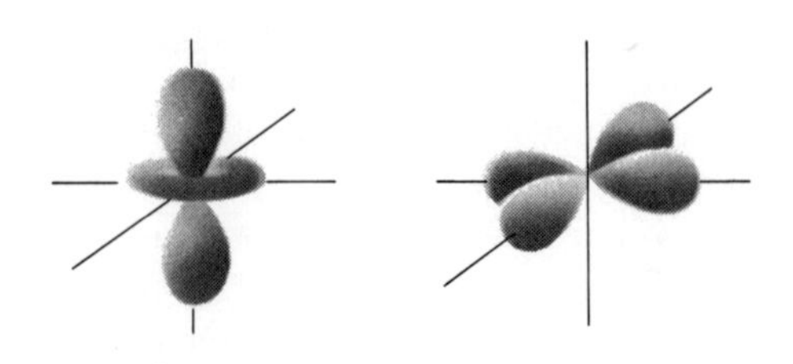

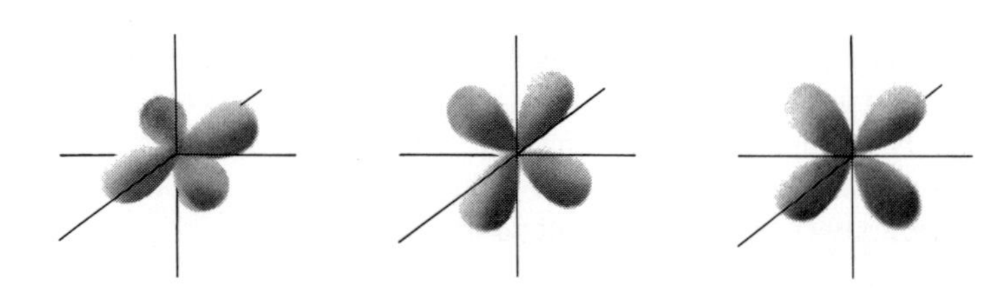

Figure 3-5 *The d orbitals.*

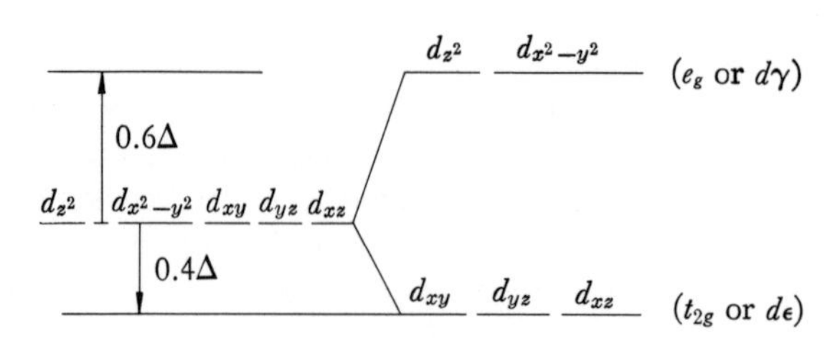

Figure 3-6 *Crystal field splitting of the d orbitals in an octahedral complex.*

electron-ligand repulsions is to raise the energy of the $d_{x^2-y^2}$ and d_{z^2} ($d\gamma$ or e_g level) relative to the d_{xy}, d_{xz}, d_{yz} ($d\epsilon$ or t_{2g} level) orbitals. This can be represented by the scheme shown in Fig. 3-6.

For an ion with a filled (or empty) d shell there would be no net effect. It therefore follows that the energy rise of the two $d\gamma$ orbitals must just equal the energy drop of the three $d\epsilon$ orbitals. Thus, the values -0.4Δ and $+0.6\Delta$ can be assigned to the $d\epsilon$ and $d\gamma$ levels, respectively. An ion with five unpaired d electrons will also show no net effect. For hydrated ions of the first transition series the electrons usually remain unpaired as long as possible (a naïve statement of Hund's rule of maximum multiplicity). $Co^{3+}(aq)$, which is diamagnetic,[37] is a notable exception. In the second and third transition series the electrons are more frequently paired than not. The ions Ti^{3+}, V^{3+}, and Cr^{3+} correspond to having one, two, and three d electrons in the $d\epsilon$ level. In Mn^{3+} and Fe^{3+} one and two additional electrons would be placed in the $d\gamma$ levels. With Co^{3+} the six d electrons pair in the $d\epsilon$ level, which gives a stabilization of $6 \times 0.4\Delta$ minus the pairing energy. Sc^{3+}, Fe^{3+}, and Ga^{3+} should show no stabilization effect.

It must be noted that Δ is not a constant but instead varies from ion to ion and depends on the ligand involved. Ions of $+2$ charge, for example, have a lower Δ value than those of $+3$ charge. Some typical values for Δ (kilocalories per mole) for hydrated ions are V^{++}, 36; V^{3+}, 50; Cr^{++}, 40; and Cr^{3+}, 50.

Orgel has argued that in the absence of a crystal field effect one expects a smooth rise in ΔH_h° as the atomic number increases and radius decreases in a series of ions of the same charge. (This assumes a smooth variation in radius, which may not be quite true.) Holmes and McClure[38] have given plots for the $+2$ and $+3$ ions, and the effect seems to be real. The curves taken from their paper are reproduced in Fig. 3-7. The maxima and minima occur in the expected way, as predicted by the simple theory. These results then suggest another refinement which might be made in calculation of hydration energies.

Most urgently needed are experimental data leading to more detailed and quantitative information about the structure and species present in the solutions. There appears to be hope that Raman, NMR, X-ray, and relaxation spectrometry methods will shed more light on the questions to be answered. A search for new tools of investigation may be required, however, to get at the finer details of the problem.

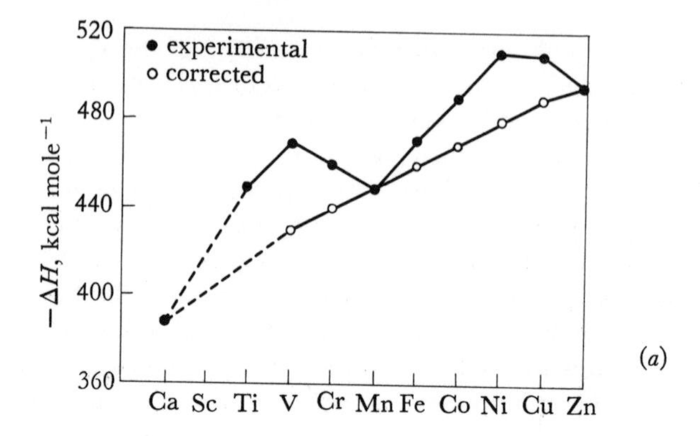

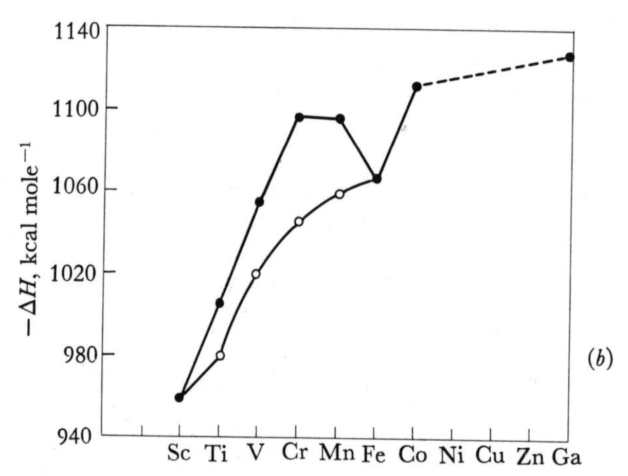

Figure 3-7 *Crystal field effects and heats of hydration; (a) divalent ions; (b) trivalent ions.* [*From O. G. Holmes and D. S. McClure, J. Chem. Phys.*, **26**, 1686 (1957).]

• 3-6 Models for Calculating the Hydration Entropy of Ions

Eley and Evans [31] have given a fairly detailed statistical-mechanical treatment of the entropy of ion hydration. Here we shall indicate only the general ideas and not consider the detailed calculations. An examination of the ΔH_h° and ΔS_h° data shows an approximate proportionality between the quantities, with ΔS_h° greater (more negative) as ΔH_h° becomes greater (more negative). This is qualitatively understandable because the increase in the interaction energy means more restriction on the bound water and thus a loss of entropy. Eley and Evans suggest the following steps to be evaluated:

1. The monatomic gaseous ion is transferred from the gas phase, thereby losing all translational motion and thus its gaseous entropy. This term, $S(T)^i(g)$, can be evaluated accurately from the Sackur-Tetrode equation mentioned in Chap. 2.

2. The presence of the ion changes the water molecules of pure water to a new state in the first coordination sphere of the ion, which gives an entropy change $\Delta S(aq)$.

3. The ion charge will change the entropy of more distant water molecules. This entropy change, ΔS_{BC}, can be obtained from the Born equation by using the values of the radii used for the ΔH_h° calculation.

4. The ion plus its hydration shell is now allowed to move in the solution, which gives an entropy increase $S(T)^i(s)$. The over-all ΔS_h° then becomes

$$\Delta S_h^\circ = -S(T)^i(g) + S(T)^i(s) + \Delta S_{BC} + \Delta S(aq)$$

The calculation of $\Delta S(aq)$ involves changes in vibrational, lateral, translational, and librational (restricted rotational) states. The restricted rotation of the water is the largest single term in $\Delta S(aq)$ and the main one for ± 1 ions. For $+2$ and $+3$ ions all the terms are important. To calculate $S(T)^i(s)$ the idea that the solvent has a quasi-crystalline lattice is invoked. This means that not all possible positions in the solution are available to the ions and, thus, not all of $S(T)^i(g)$ is regained.

Some typical values of the various terms and their sums are given in Table 3-2. The $-\Delta S_h^\circ$(exptl.) values were obtained from those of Latimer (Ref. 9, Chap. 2) by taking $\bar{S}_{H^+}{}^\circ = -2.1$, 1 atm, for the gaseous standard state and hypothetical 1 *m* for the solute standard state. (These standard states are the ones used by Eley and Evans.) The agreement between calculated and experimental values for the sums ($Li^+ + F^-$, for example) is the criterion which should be used to check the validity of the calculations. The agreement is somewhat poorer if comparison is based on the more recent values of Latimer rather than the older values used by Eley and Evans. In any case, however, the discrepancies are probably not unreasonable if the difficulties in the calculation and the errors in the experimental values are considered.

Table 3-2 Eley and Evans entropy calculations at 298°K

Ion	$\Delta S(aq)$	ΔS_{BC}	$S(T)^i(s)$	$S(T)^i(g)$	$-\Delta S_h^\circ$ (calc.)	$-\Delta S_h^\circ$ (exptl.)
F^-	−22.8	−2.4	24.5	34.5	35.2	34
Cl^-	−10.9	−2.1	25.2	36.4	24.2	21
Br^-	−0.3	−2.1	25.8	38.8	15.4	17
I^-	+7.3	−2.0	26.0	40.1	8.8	12
Li^+	−23.1	−2.7	22.6	31.5	34.7	30
Na^+	−15.3	−2.6	24.7	35.1	28.3	23
K^+	−8.1	−2.4	25.3	36.6	21.8	14
Mg^{++}	−50.9	−11.0	24.7	35.2	72.4	67
Ca^{++}	−39.7	−10.4	25.3	36.7	61.5	54
Ba^{++}	−27.2	−9.3	26.0	40.4	50.9	41
Zn^{++}	−47.3	−11.0	25.7	38.3	70.9	68
Al^{3+}	−66.7	−26.6	24.9	35.7	104	116
Fe^{3+}	−60.5	−25.6	25.8	37.7	98	116

One feature that the Eley and Evans entropy calculation suggests is that positive and negative ions of the same crystal radius (K^+ and F^-) have different hydrational entropies, although the difference comes out less than in Latimer's treatment. This is in contrast with the Eley-Evans calculation of the enthalpies in which no asymmetry was found. The difference arises in the more negative entropy associated with the restricted rotation of H_2O attached to the negative ion.

The Eley and Evans model also suggests that one should not expect a simple relation between ΔS_h° and some charge/radius function. In a later article,[39] Eley points out the interesting fact that the entropy of hydration for rare-gas atoms is surprisingly large. This cannot be due to the effects of charge but is consistent with the idea that not all sites in the quasi-crystalline structure of water are available to the solute. Presumably an uncharged species is even more restricted as to sites than a charged species, since the "lattice" is due to charge interactions.

A somewhat different approach to the properties of aqueous solutions has been made by Frank in several papers.[40–44] A brief outline of his ideas is given in the following discussion. He noted that the entropy of solution of inert gases in polar and nonpolar solvents is negative and that it is more negative in the polar solvent. In a nonpolar solvent the inert gas loses freedom of movement in the solvent, which gives rise to a negative entropy charge. Although the solvent may expand and thereby give rise to a positive entropy change, the former effect outweighs the latter.

In water the inert gas, in addition to losing freedom of motion, causes an ordering of the nearby water (termed by Frank "iceberg formation") that leads to a larger negative ΔS term. This effect is larger as the size of the inert-gas atom is larger. That the ΔS of solution becomes more positive as the temperature increases suggests that the icebergs are "melting," or less order is present. The rather high partial molal heat capacities are consistent with the melting idea.

In addition to the iceberg formation there will be a structure-breaking effect on more distant water molecules that will give an entropy increase. The structure breaking is due in general to the fact that the iceberg arrangement will not easily fit into the usual water structure. Again a net entropy decrease results. The iceberg may represent a clathrate structure of the type, discussed by Pauling,[45] in which the gas molecule is "trapped" in a solvent "cage" formed by hydrogen bonding. The forces between the gas and solvent are of the Van der Waals type.

Frank notes (as did Eley) the apparently more negative entropy for solution of rare-gas atoms than gaseous ions of the same size. For example, ΔS_h° for $K^+ + Cl^-$ is -52 eu, whereas for two Ar atoms ΔS_h° is -60 eu on a comparable basis. This suggests a greater structure-breaking effect for the ions than for the inert gas.

Consideration of viscosity, heat capacities, compressibilities, and other phenomena also leads to a similar picture. This picture may be summarized by the drawing of Fig. 3-8. Here the ion is surrounded by the three regions *A*, *B*, and *C*. *A* represents a region of water immobilization or freezing; *B* is a region of structure breaking or melting; and *C* represents undisturbed or possibly slightly more ordered water. The *B* region results from the conflicting effects of the ion-water interaction in region *A* and the water-water interaction in region *C*. On the basis of the various kinds of evidence, Frank describes the ions as follows:

1. Cations smaller or more highly charged than K^+ are net structure-formers.

2. K^+ is slightly structure breaking, and the effect increases from K^+ to Cs^+.

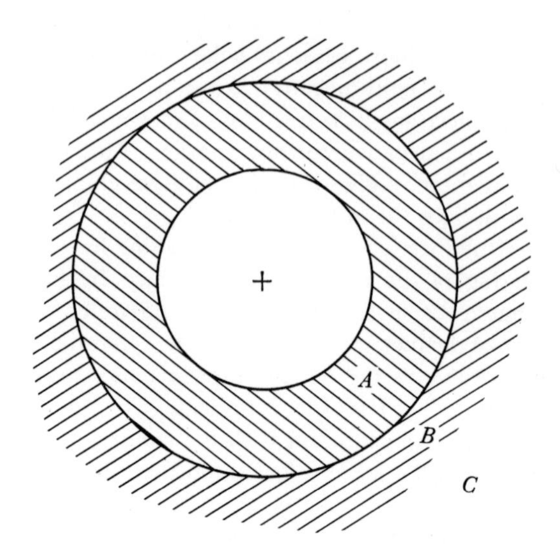

Figure 3-8 *Frank's model for a hydrated ion.*

3. F^- is a structure-former, but Cl^-, Br^-, I^- are increasingly structure-breakers.

4. NO_3^- and ClO_4^- are strong structure breakers, and $SO_4^=$ is less so.

5. OH^- is a structure-former.

Although the model remains a somewhat qualitative one, it incorporates most of the known features of ionic solutions. No doubt more work will be done on the quantitative aspects in the future.

• 3-7 Summary

We have concentrated our attention on only a few of the many phenomena observable in aqueous solutions, mainly those that seem to be of interest to inorganic chemists. A complete understanding, of course, requires understanding of all the phenomena. Studies on heat capacities, transport phenomena, dielectric effects, diffusion, and compressibilities, for example, all shed light on the solution properties, and these effects must finally be accounted for by the theory.

The qualitative picture which has emerged from our discussions recognizes the importance of the structure of water and its changes when ions are placed in it. Both experimental and theoretical work are needed in this area. The concept of the hydrated ion as a species seems to be a useful one. New techniques for studying hydrated ions, as well as better methods for calculating the interactions of ions and water molecules, are needed.

The region between the hydrated ion and the bulk solvent is perhaps the least well understood. There may, of course, be no sharp division into regions, so that the boundaries are vague. Considerable improvement in the reliability of the thermodynamic data is needed in order to test models more carefully. The area of activity coefficients is vital to solving the reliability problem, since without a good knowledge of their behavior the true standard-state values cannot be obtained.

Up to now we have assumed that we are dealing only with separate hydrated ions and that no additional complications exist. In the next chapters we shall consider some of the many complications to the simple picture. We shall start with reactions involving the acidity of the solutions—in particular, with hydrolysis and some of its consequences.

References

1. J. Morgan and B. E. Warren, *J. Chem. Phys.*, **6,** 666 (1938).
2. G. W. Brady and W. J. Romanow, *J. Chem. Phys.*, **32,** 306 (1960).
3. J. D. Bernal and R. H. Fowler, *J. Chem. Phys.*, **1,** 515 (1933).
4. L. Pauling, *The Nature of the Chemical Bond*, 3d ed., Cornell University Press, Ithaca, N.Y., 1960, p. 464.
5. C. H. Collie, J. B. Hasted, and D. M. Ritson, *Proc. Phys. Soc.* (London), **60,** 145 (1948).
6. G. W. Brady and J. T. Krause, *J. Chem. Phys.*, **27,** 304 (1957).
7. G. W. Brady, *J. Chem. Phys.*, **28,** 464 (1958).
8. J. W. Schultz and D. F. Hornig, *J. Phys. Chem.*, **65,** 2131 (1961).
9. G. E. Walrafen, *J. Chem. Phys.*, **36,** 90 (1962).
10. M. Eigen and L. DeMaeyer, *Proc. Roy. Soc. (London)*, **A247,** 505 (1958).
11. S. Meiboom, *J. Chem. Phys.*, **34,** 375 (1961).
12. O. Redlich and G. C. Hood, *Discussions Faraday Soc.*, No. **24,** 87 (1957).
13. J. O'M. Bockris, *Quart. Rev. (London)*, **3,** 173 (1949).
14. J. P. Hunt and H. Taube, *J. Chem. Phys.*, **19,** 602 (1951).
15. H. H. Baldwin and H. Taube, *J. Chem. Phys.*, **33,** 206 (1960).
16. H. Taube, *J. Phys. Chem.*, **58,** 523 (1954).
17. H. M. Feder, "Ionic Hydration: An Isotopic Fractionation Technique," Ph.D. Thesis, University of Chicago, 1954.

18. J. A. Jackson, J. F. Lemons, and H. Taube, *J. Chem. Phys.*, **32,** 553 (1960).
19. R. E. Connick and R. E. Poulson, *J. Chem. Phys.*, **30,** 759 (1959).
20. R. E. Connick and E. D. Stover, *J. Phys. Chem.*, **65,** 2075 (1961).
21. E. E. Genser, *Lawrence Radiation Lab. Rept.*, **UCRL 9846,** University of California, Berkeley, 1961.
22. T. J. Swift, *Lawrence Radiation Lab. Rept.*, **UCRL 10274,** University of California, Berkeley, 1962.
23. E. C. Baughan, *J. Chem. Soc.*, 1403 (1940).
24. E. Wicke, M. Eigen, and T. Ackermann, *Z. Physik. Chem. (Frankfurt)*, **1,** 340 (1954).
25. R. P. Bell, *The Proton in Chemistry*, Cornell University Press, Ithaca, N.Y., 1959, p. 83.
26. M. Born, *Physik. Z.*, **1,** 45 (1920).
27. W. M. Latimer, K. S. Pitzer, and C. M. Slansky, *J. Chem. Phys.*, **7,** 108 (1939).
28. W. M. Latimer, *J. Chem. Phys.*, **23,** 90 (1955).
29. E. L. King, *J. Phys. Chem.*, **63,** 1070 (1959).
30. R. M. Noyes, *J. Am. Chem. Soc.*, **84,** 513 (1962).
31. D. D. Eley and M. G. Evans, *Trans. Faraday Soc.*, **34,** 1093 (1938).
32. E. J. W. Verwey, *Rec. Trav. Chim.*, **61,** 127 (1942).
33. A. D. Buckingham, *Discussions Faraday Soc.*, No. **24,** 151 (1957).
34. O. Ya Samoilov, *Discussions Faraday Soc.*, No. **24,** 141 (1957).
35. L. E. Orgel, *J. Chem. Soc.*, 4756 (1952).
36. L. E. Orgel, *Transition Metal Chemistry*, Wiley, New York, 1960.
37. H. L. Friedman, J. P. Hunt, R. A. Plane, and H. Taube, *J. Am. Chem. Soc.*, **73,** 4028 (1951).
38. O. G. Holmes and D. S. McClure, *J. Chem. Phys.*, **26,** 1686 (1957).
39. D. D. Eley, *Trans. Faraday Soc.*, **40,** 184 (1944).
40. H. S. Frank, *J. Chem. Phys.*, **13,** 478 (1945).
41. H. S. Frank and M. W. Evans, *J. Chem. Phys.*, **13,** 507 (1945).
42. H. S. Frank and W. Y. Wen, *Discussions Faraday Soc.*, No. **24,** 133 (1957).
43. H. S. Frank, *Proc. Roy. Soc. (London)*, **A247,** 481 (1958).
44. H. S. Frank and A. S. Quist, *J. Chem. Phys.*, **34,** 604 (1961).
45. L. Pauling, *The Nature of the Chemical Bond*, 3d ed., Cornell University Press, Ithaca, N.Y., 1960, p. 469.

4

Hydrolysis and Related Phenomena

Up to now we have assumed that ions in solution are associated with water molecules independently of one another and that no reactions other than hydration are involved. We have seen that, even under these conditions, the situation is a complicated and incompletely understood one. In actual fact, the picture is far more complicated in general than has been indicated. In this chapter we shall consider complications due to hydrolytic reactions of the cations, assuming we can neglect specific effects of the anions present. Such an assumption may often not be justified, and we shall consider this aspect further in the next chapter.

• 4-1 Simple Hydrolysis

The simplest and most familiar hydrolytic process is that of "simple" hydrolysis. The process is often represented by an equation such as

$$Al^{3+} + H_2O \leftrightarrows Al(OH)^{++} + H^+$$

which implies that an aqueous solution of Al^{3+} ions gives an acidic solution (provided that anion hydrolysis is absent or less in amount).

There are several alternative ways of looking at the process, and the reaction may also be written, for example, as follows:

$$Al(H_2O)_6{}^{3+} + H_2O \rightleftharpoons Al(H_2O)_5OH^{++} + H_3O^+$$

or

$$Al(H_2O)_6{}^{3+} \rightleftharpoons Al(H_2O)_5(OH)^{++} + H^+$$

or

$$Al^{3+} + OH^- \rightleftharpoons Al(OH)^{++}$$

or

$$Al(H_2O)_6{}^{3+} + OH^- \rightleftharpoons Al(H_2O)_5OH^{++} + H_2O$$

and so on.

The different representations reflect various attempts to indicate the species present and the different possible mechanisms for the process. These various equations are, of course, basically equivalent, and to some extent one chooses the equation most convenient for his purpose. As usual, there is very little direct information on the nature of the species actually present or the mechanism of the process.

At the present time, it is generally believed that the process can continue in a series of reactions. This idea can be represented by the equations

$$\begin{aligned} Al(H_2O)_6{}^{3+} &\rightleftharpoons Al(H_2O)_5OH^{++} + H^+ \\ Al(H_2O)_5(OH)^{++} &\rightleftharpoons Al(H_2O)_4(OH)_2{}^+ + H^+ \\ Al(H_2O)_4(OH)_2{}^+ &\rightleftharpoons Al(H_2O)_3(OH)_3 + H^+ \\ &\vdots \\ Al(H_2O)(OH)_5{}^= &\rightleftharpoons Al(OH)_6{}^{3-} + H^+ \end{aligned}$$

Such a scheme has the advantage of representing amphoteric behavior as a special case of hydrolysis rather than as a separate phenomenon. In this approach, one can speak of the acidity of the aquo ion as being responsible for the behavior observed. This picture is essentially the one suggested by Brönsted many years ago. One might perhaps wish to represent the H^+ ion in a more detailed way ($H_9O_4{}^+$, for example); but since we are mainly concerned with the metal ion, there is no great advantage in doing so. The interconversion of species differing only by a $H^+(aq)$ is apparently rapid, and thus equilibria of this sort should be established rapidly.

In some cases the ionic species are represented quite differently.

In fairly concentrated acid solutions we usually represent the species present by formulas such as $Cr(H_2O)_6^{3+}$ and $Mg(H_2O)_4^{++}$. However, for some ions the formulas used are often quite different, for example, UO_2^{++}, VO_2^{++}, BiO^+, SbO^+, PuO_2^{++}, and ZrO^{++}. Much of the "evidence" for these seems to come from the existence of solid compounds containing these ions and their behavior as ions of relatively low charge. One might regard them as arising from extensive hydrolysis of hypothetical ions in a manner such as

$$U(H_2O)_6^{6+} \rightarrow UO_2^{++} + 4H^+ + 4H_2O$$

(Perhaps the UO_2^{++} should be written as $UO_2(H_2O)_4^{++}$.)

An extreme example of this point of view can be shown as

$$S(H_2O)_4^{6+} \rightarrow SO_4^{=} + 8H^+$$

Such pictures are generally hypothetical, since equilibria between the various forms are not observed. It is interesting that O^{18} studies [1] do support the formulation UO_2^{++}. Most of these ions appear to give complicated species at lower acidities. We shall not consider properties of such ions in detail in this book.

• 4-2 Polymerization

A further complication appears to be rather common, especially for highly charged ions. The hydrolyzed species such as $Al(H_2O)_5OH^{++}$ can be considered to polymerize by essentially a "condensation" process as shown by the equation

$$2Al(H_2O)_5OH^{++} \rightarrow [(H_2O)_5Al{-}O{-}Al(H_2O)_5]^{4+} + H_2O$$

Such a process could in principle continue almost indefinitely by further loss of H^+ ions and formation of *bridges.* The polymeric species themselves would be expected to be involved in equilibria involving H^+ ions, for example

$$[(H_2O)_5Al{-}O{-}Al(H_2O)_5]^{4+} \rightleftharpoons [(H_2O)_5Al{-}O{-}Al(H_2O)_4(OH)]^{3+} + H^+$$

or

$$[(H_2O)_5Al{-}O{-}Al(H_2O)_5]^{4+} + H^+ \rightleftharpoons [(H_2O)_5Al{-}\overset{\overset{\displaystyle H}{|}}{O}{-}Al(H_2O)_5]^{5+}$$

The terms "ol" and "oxo" are often used in referring to the OH and O bridges, respectively, and the process is sometimes called olation. It is easily seen that an extremely large number of such species can be imagined to exist. The formation of the polymers might be expected to be much slower than the simple hydrolyses, since more drastic rearrangements occur. Again, very few data on the nature of the species or the reaction mechanisms are available.

• 4-3 Inner-Sphere and Outer-Sphere Complexes

Still another problem has received considerable attention in recent times. It is possible to imagine that an OH^- ion might not be in the first coordination sphere of the ion, but rather separated from it by one or more water molecules. It seems to be very difficult to decide how many intermediate water molecules are required before the OH^- ion is "free," although it appears reasonable that the forces of attraction will be rather small beyond one water molecule. The situation is sometimes described in terms of inner-sphere and outer-sphere complexes. An example of an inner-sphere complex would be $Al(H_2O)_5OH^{++}$, whereas the outer-sphere complex could be written as $[Al(H_2O)_6{}^{3+} \cdot OH^-]^{++}$.

In most cases the methods used will not distinguish between these possibilities. Spectral methods would be most likely to be of use in this connection. Such a study was made for the Tl^+ case.[2] A value of K_{eq} for the reaction $Tl^+ + H_2O \rightleftharpoons TlOH + H^+$ of ca. 10^{-13} has been reported, but the Raman work cited in Ref. 2 detects no Tl—OH bond vibrations. This suggests that if the species exists, it has essentially ionic bonds.

• 4-4 Hydrolysis Data

Let us now consider in more detail the simple hydrolysis process. Unfortunately, it is not easy to separate the simple from the more complex processes occurring in solution, which means that unambiguous data are scarce. In addition, in order to obtain true thermodynamic values for the equilibria postulated, one often requires more information about activity coefficients than is now available. Uncertainties about the hydrolytic process and activity coefficients are largely responsible for the errors in the hydration data discussed in Chap. 3. The methods most commonly used to study such processes involve pH measurements using various techniques. If the spectra of the various species are different, then spectrophotometric methods may be applicable. A discussion and many references to other methods for studying ionic equilibria are given in a book by Rossotti and Rossotti.[3]

A convenient source of data up to the middle of 1957 is the Chemical Society compilation.[4] An examination of these reported data shows at once the difficulties involved. In most cases there are discordant values even when the results are presumed to apply to the same experimental conditions. There are relatively few data obtained in the standard states we have been using, mainly because of the activity coefficient problem mentioned earlier. The Scandinavian workers[5] often use a medium of 3 *M* $NaClO_4$ in their work, which presumably keeps the activity coefficients constant during the measurements. It seems rather unlikely, however, that comparisons of different ions can be meaningful at such high salt concentrations, since rather specific effects on the different activity coefficients involved are expected.

There seems to be no doubt that much more careful work is needed on this problem, preferably to try to obtain data relevant to the hypothetical molar or molal standard states. Consider the equilibrium reaction

$$Al(H_2O)_6{}^{3+} \rightleftharpoons Al(H_2O)_5OH^{++} + H^+$$

The thermodynamic equilibrium constant as usually written in simplified notation would be

$$K_{eq} = \frac{[AlOH^{++}]\gamma_{AlOH^{++}}[H^+]\gamma_{H^+}}{[Al^{3+}]\gamma_{Al^{3+}}}$$

Actually, since single-ion activity coefficients are not known, the anions should be included and the corresponding activity coefficients should be used. The expression might then be written as, for example,

$$K_{eq} = \frac{[AlOH(ClO_4)_2][HClO_4]\gamma_{AlOH(ClO_4)_2}\gamma_{HClO_4}}{[Al(ClO_4)_3]\gamma_{Al(ClO_4)_3}}$$

To obtain the K values, it is necessary either to know the γ values under the experimental conditions or to be able to extrapolate the data to zero salt concentration, where the γ values become unity. The lack of knowledge concerning the proper activity coefficients or extrapolation is probably the biggest problem which must be overcome before the data are really useful for theoretical understanding of the equilibria.

In addition, one needs $\Delta H°$ and $\Delta S°$ values for the processes in order to arrive at a sound theoretical explanation of the data. In principle, ΔH can be obtained from calorimetric studies (preferably) or from the temperature coefficient of the equilibrium constant. In practice, neither approach is easy or without problems, and few reliable data appear to exist. Some selected data from Ref. 4 are given in Table 4-1.

Table 4-1 *Hydrolysis data for metal ions*

(Temp = 25 °C and μ = 0 unless otherwise noted)

Ion	$-\log K_h$, pK	ΔH_h, kcal mole^{-1}	ΔS_h, eu	Remarks
Li^+	13.8			
Na^+	14.6			
Mg^{++}	11.4			
Ca^{++}	12.7			
Sc^{3+}	4.61			$\mu = 0.01$
Th^{4+}	3.82			
V^{3+}	2.9			
Cr^{3+}	3.82	9.4	14.1	
Fe^{3+}	2.17	10.4	25	
Co^{3+}	1.74	10	25	$\mu = 1$
Ni^{++}	10.6			
Cu^{++}	7.5			
Ag^+	11.7			
Zn^{++}	9.7			
Cd^{++}	7.6			$\mu = 1$
Cd^{++}	9.0			$\mu = 3$
Hg^{++}	2.49			
Al^{3+}	5.02			Average of 6 values
Ga^{3+}	2.92			$\mu = 0.5$
In^{3+}	3.70			"Dilute" solution
Tl^{3+}	1.14			$\mu = 3$
Sn^{++}	1.7, 2.1			
Pb^{++}	6.2			

One might ask what sort of results could have been predicted. A very naïve approach based on regarding the process as involving ionization of the aquo complex is often used to describe the situation:

$$M(H_2O)_x^{n+} \rightleftharpoons M(H_2O)_{x-1}(OH)^{(n-1)+} + H^+$$

The argument is made that the H^+ will ionize off most readily the higher the positive ionic charge and the smaller the radius of the metal ion. Such an argument either ignores ΔS and hydration effects or assumes that they have no net effect on the trends. In a gross sort of way the data do follow the suggested trend. The pK ($-\log K$) values are generally smaller the higher the charge and larger the greater the radius.

In the case of $+1$ ions, hydrolysis, if real, is very slight and shows an apparent increase in pK as ionic radius increases. Many investigators are inclined to ascribe the measured effects to activity coefficient changes rather than to hydrolysis. Others refer to outer-sphere complexes as being formed. The situation with the alkaline earth ions is more involved. Be^{++} appears to show a complex hydrolysis with polymer formation and no simple hydrolysis. The reported pK value for Mg^{++} is smaller than for the $+1$ ions, but still a small effect is involved. The remainder of the alkaline earths show even smaller effects, perhaps with pK increasing with increasing size. Comparisons in the series V^{3+}, Cr^{3+}, Fe^{3+}, and Co^{3+} (radii decreasing) gives the respective pK values 2.9, 3.82, 2.17, and 1.74 (μ = 1).

One might say that Cr^{3+} is out of line for some reason. Since OH^- presumably produces a weaker field than H_2O, one might expect that ions with the most crystal field stabilization would be the least hydrolyzed. This would account for $Cr(H_2O)_6{}^{3+}$ being a weaker acid than V^{3+} or Fe^{3+}. Co^{3+} is presumably about the same size as Fe^{3+} but should have a large crystal field stabilization. It appears, however, to be a stronger acid. The amphoteric nature of Cr(III) compared to Fe(III) is also not in accord with the simple crystal field idea. The ΔH and ΔS values show that the $T\,\Delta S$ term difference is important between Cr^{3+} and Fe^{3+}, and, in fact, most of the difference in the pK values resides in this $T\,\Delta S$ term. Al^{3+}, which is smaller than the $+3$ ions just mentioned, is an even weaker acid. The trend in the series Al^{3+}, Ga^{3+}, In^{3+}, and Tl^{3+} is just the opposite of that expected on the basis of radii.

In the absence of more extensive data on the thermodynamics of hydrolysis it does not seem very profitable to try to account for the details observed. Since the process is such a fundamental one, it does seem well worthwhile that investigators spend considerable research effort to try to clear up these details.

• 4-5 Successive Ionization

Although data are sometimes given for the successive ionization steps written earlier, they are in general even less reliable than those for the first step. It is usually supposed that the values of K for succeeding steps will be smaller than for the preceding ones. This situation is very much complicated by the polymerization indicated previously. The decreasing trend may be found for Ga^{3+}. For Hg^{2+} the data are conflicting on this point. For Sc^{3+} at $\mu = 1$ the K values for the first and second steps are reported to be equal. There are too few reliable results to decide on general trends. In principle, the best approach would be to find methods which give direct information on the structure of the species formed. Some sort of spectral method which will work in dilute solutions is needed. In concentrated solutions infrared, Raman, X-ray, and NMR spectroscopy would be useful. These methods have been applied, but mainly to the questions of polymerization and anionic complexes.

• 4-6 Polymeric Species

The subject of polymeric cationic species has received considerable attention in recent work. It does seem likely, for example, that a formula for "aluminum hydroxide" such as $Al(H_2O)_3(OH)_3$ is not a good representation for the usual gelatinous material observed. Many "hydroxides" resemble the hydroxide of Al^{3+} in general appearance and behavior. Polymeric hydrogen-bonded structures would appear to be more likely.

In solution there are various kinds of evidence for the existence of related polymeric species of the sort indicated previously. To begin with, many conventional hydrolysis studies seem to require them to account for the experimental data. Sillén [6] has given much attention to this problem and has emphasized its importance. The activity coefficient problems, as usual, and the general complexities of the solutions make it hard to get a clear picture.

Somewhat different approaches have also been made to this problem. Ultracentrifuge studies, for example, have been made on Bi(III), Hf(IV), and Zr(IV) by Kraus and co-workers.[7] Their results definitely indicate polymeric species, possibly of the form $[Bi(OH)_2]_6(ClO_4)_2^{4+}$ in the case of Bi(III), in which ClO_4^- ions are included in the polymer. Light-scattering methods [8] and X-ray analysis [9] also lead to similar conclusions. Magnetic studies, based on the change in magnetic moment that might occur, have been used to investigate polymeric ions. Polymers based on this method are reported for U^{4+}, Fe^{3+}, and Ni^{++}. (See Ref. 10 for data on Fe^{3+}.) Laswick and Plane [11] have used ion-exchange resins to separate various Cr(III) species including what appears to be a dimer. Changes in this system are also generally slow.

Experiments of the sort mentioned above, and others, leave little doubt that polymeric species do exist. They seem to be most likely for highly charged and/or small ions. Polymeric cationic species are reported for Be(II), Sc(III), Ce(IV), Zr(IV), Hf(IV), Th(IV), Cr(III), Mo(V), U(VI), Fe(III), Co(III), Ni(II), Ru(IV), Cu(II), Zn(II), Al(III), Ga(III), In(III), Sn(II), Sn(IV), Pb(II), Sb(V), Bi(III), and others, which suggests that the phenomenon is quite general. Equilibrium constants for the majority of these ions are not known in general, nor are the structural details. It is clear that attention must be paid to the possible existence of such species, especially at low acidities.

• 4-7 Anionic Species

Polymeric anionic species have been known for a long time. The well known iso- and heteropoly anions formed by P(V), Cr(VI), Mo(VI), W(VI), V(V), and others have been extensively studied. Simple anionic species are often postulated in forms such as CrO_2^- or $Cr(OH)_4^-$ to represent amphoteric behavior. We shall not consider the usual iso- and heteropoly anion systems here. Rather, we shall look briefly at what is thought to be known about monomeric species and some anionic polymers.

Raman studies [12] indicate the existence of tetrahedral $Zn(OH)_4^{=}$ and $Al(OH)_4^-$ in concentrated base solutions. The well-known solubility of many hydroxides in excess OH^- is usually interpreted in terms of anionic species, though usually the formulas are not known. It seems likely that polymeric anions are often formed. The nature of these anions is expected to vary with OH^- concentration. Values for K and/or evidence for complexes are reported for the formation of species such as $Bi(OH)_4^-$, $Sb(OH)_6^-$, $HSb_6O_{17}^{3-}$, $Sn(OH)_6^=$, $Sn_4O_{10}^{4-}$, $Ga(OH)_4^-$, $Ga_2(OH)_8^=$, $Al(OH)_4^-$, $Al_3(OH)_{10}^-$, $Zn(OH)_3^-$, $Zn(OH)_4^=$, $Zn(OH)_6^{4-}$, $Zn_2(OH)_8^{4-}$, $Cu(OH)_3^-$, and $Cr(OH)_4^-$. A careful study of each case would be required to decide how good the evidence is for the postulated species.

It appears clear enough that hydrolytic processes for metal ions are very complex indeed. More careful and critical measurements, as well as more direct methods, are needed. As indicated earlier, a promising start has been made in the direction of new methods.

We have not made much use in this chapter of the concept of hydrolysis as a complex-formation process, although it often is convenient to do so. Hydrolysis then becomes a process of replacing H_2O by OH^- in the coordination sphere of the ion. Such a picture is most useful when comparing the replacement of H_2O by various ligands, which we shall discuss in the next chapter. As we shall see, the problems that beset the study of hydrolysis are also present in studies of other complex-forming reactions.

References

1. H. W. Crandall, *J. Chem. Phys.*, **17,** 602 (1949).
2. J. H. B. George, J. A. Rolfe, and L. A. Woodward, *Trans. Faraday Soc.*, **49,** 375 (1953).
3. F. J. C. Rossotti and H. Rossotti, *The Determination of Stability Constants*, McGraw-Hill, New York, 1961.
4. "Stability Constants," *Chem. Soc.* (*London*), **Spec. Publ. 7,** Part II.
5. G. Biedermann and L. G. Sillén, *Arkiv Kemi*, **5,** 425 (1953).
6. L. G. Sillén, *Acta. Chem. Scand.*, **8,** 299 (1954).
7. R. W. Holmberg, K. A. Kraus, and J. S. Johnson, *J. Am. Chem. Soc.*, **78,** 5506 (1956).
8. R. S. Tobias and S. Y. Tyree, Jr., *J. Am. Chem. Soc.*, **82,** 3244 (1960).
9. H. A. Levy, M. D. Danford, and P. A. Agron, *J. Chem. Phys.*, **31,** 1458 (1959).
10. L. N. Mulay and P. W. Selwood, *J. Am. Chem. Soc.*, **76,** 6207 (1954).
11. J. A. Laswick and R. A. Plane, *J. Am. Chem. Soc.*, **81,** 3564 (1959).
12. E. R. Lippincott, J. A. Psellos, and M. C. Tobin, *J. Chem. Phys.*, **20,** 536 (1952).

5

Equilibria Involving Complex Ions and Molecules

The subject of complex chemistry has been one of the major areas of research in inorganic chemistry for many years. It will not be possible to cover in detail all the many aspects of this subject or even to mention all the phenomena that are observed. We shall try to look at some of the basic concepts and problems rather closely instead of trying to survey the known complexes and their properties. Much more detailed information can be found in the many recent books and reviews.[1-7]

• 5-1 Dilute Solutions

Let us first consider to what extent ions are independent of one another in solutions. One way of looking at the question is to ask about the nature of the forces between ions. It is not possible to give a detailed account of the forces involved, but they are electrical in nature and include at least the London or dispersion forces, Coulomb forces, and the quantum-mechanical forces involved in chemical binding. These forces all fall off with increasing separations of the ions, but they are not zero at finite distances. In this sense the ions cannot be completely independent in real solutions.

The usual approach is to define an ideal state in which the ions do behave as independent species. The concept of the infinitely dilute solution is introduced as a reference for independent behavior, since the forces involved should go to zero at infinite separation. An infinitely dilute solution is not, however, a very useful one as a practical reference, since functions such as the free energy of the solute go to negative infinity in such a solution. For this reason the practical reference state (standard state) is often taken to be that of a *hypothetical* 1 m (or 1 M) solution in which the ions are independent as at infinite dilution. Such behavior may be referred to as ideal behavior. This ideal behavior will be found at all concentrations and temperatures for the hypothetical solution. The species in these solutions will, for example, obey the law of mass action.

The usual thermodynamic approach, then, considers deviations from ideal behavior as evidence for interactions in the solution. Most frequently, for the subject in which we are interested, deviations from the law of mass action are used as the criteria for nonideal behavior. According to the law of mass action, equilibrium-constant expressions should involve concentrations of the species involved, and the K_{eq} values should be constant (at constant temperature and pressure) for all concentrations of the species at equilibrium. In real solutions this is not the case and the deviations can be treated in terms of activity coefficients. Thus for an equilibrium such as

$$A + B \rightleftharpoons C + D$$

we have

$$K_{eq} = \frac{[C][D]\gamma_C\gamma_D}{[A][B]\gamma_A\gamma_B}$$

where the γ's are the relevant activity coefficients and the brackets refer to concentrations.

The great contribution of Debye and Hückel was to provide a theoretical basis for the activity coefficients in dilute solutions. It should be mentioned, however, that the thermodynamic treatment alone does not give direct information on the species present in solution and that a formal treatment can be given without a detailed knowledge of the species. The Debye-Hückel theory provides a way of getting the γ values and thus testing the existence of proposed species by finding whether experimental data are consistent with a particular formulation. There is no assumption that 100% dissociation of a salt occurs, but the theory permits calculating the γ values for the ions that may be present.

The Debye-Hückel picture that arises for these dilute solutions is that each separate ion is surrounded by a rapidly fluctuating cloud of ions, with a slight preponderance of those with opposite charge, and that the ions of any pair are relatively far apart. Most workers in the field would say that the ions are relatively free and that several water molecules separate them. We have pointed out before that the exact nature of the hydrated ions present is usually not known; the Debye-Hückel theory does not treat this question.

It seems fair to say that dilute solutions can in principle be understood in some detail. A precise definition of "dilute" is hard to give, and it varies with the charges on the ions in question. An upper limit may be 10^{-2} *M*, and 10^{-3} *M* or 10^{-4} *M* may be more realistic, especially for ions of charge greater than unity. Dilute solutions have received much attention and thought, and we have barely scratched the surface of this subject. The reader is referred to the basic work of Harned and Owen [8] for a rigorous consideration of these problems.

• 5-2 Concentrated Solutions

Most systems of interest to inorganic chemists involve much higher concentrations than those for which the dilute-solution theory is valid. For purposes of understanding the chemistry involved, one wants to be able to separate out those factors which are due to external influences (the so-called medium effects), although the external effects are interesting and important in themselves. In principle, one might, for example, like to compare Cl^- complexes of Cr^{3+} and Fe^{3+} on the basis of intrinsic characteristics of these ions without the complications due to general interactions with the solvent and other ions. This could be done, in principle, by using a cycle involving the thermodynamic hydration quantities to obtain the quantities for the gaseous (usually hypothetical) reaction. In practice, this means that the data must be converted to apply to our chosen standard states. This, in turn, requires either a knowledge of the activity coefficients or their functional dependence on concentration. If the latter is known, then the data can be extrapolated to zero concentration to give the desired quantities. Unfortunately, the knowledge needed is often not available for the solutions of interest.

The determination of activity coefficients usually involves the same sort of experiment that is presumed to give information about the equilibria and species involved, and no separation of these is obtained. Theoretical treatments involve unknown parameters and some arbitrariness. Among the factors which need to be considered are these: How is the water structure affected by ions? What species are actually present? Most attention seems to be given to the latter question. The point involves not only questions of hydration but also questions of ion association.

We are brought back to the question of what constitutes a chemical species, and much of the argument in the literature revolves about this question. One can discuss the problem in these terms: consider oppositely charged ions separated by relatively large distances with many water molecules between them and perhaps several directly attached to each ion. We essentially have only the Debye-Hückel ion clouds as far as ion-ion interaction is concerned. If the solution is concentrated, the average distance between ions decreases and fewer water molecules separate the opposite charges. How close must the ions be before a species forms? Theoretically one might say that a minimum in the potential-energy curve must occur at some separation and that then a species can be said to exist. One then asks how deep a minimum will be required, for a shallow minimum will mean that the species has a short lifetime.

Much discussion of this subject has taken place over the years, and it seems evident that no unambiguous theoretical answer can be given. Some idea of the problems involved can be obtained by referring to the papers presented at the 1957 Faraday Society discussions.[9] Many persons have suggested that at least two types of species should be considered. The first of these is the inner-sphere complex referred to in Chap. 4. Here the negative ion is immediately adjacent to the cation and should be a normal chemical species. The second will involve the separation of the anion and cation by one or at most two water molecules (outer-sphere complex). Beyond the outer-sphere range the interactions will not be considered to give rise to a chemical species and will be treated by activity coefficient theories involving nonspecific interactions.

There is by no means agreement on this picture or its desirability. It would seem very desirable to have experimental evidence for the postulated species, but even the experimental evidence is not without ambiguities. Various methods imply various lifetimes of the species to allow detection. Redlich [10] has emphasized this point and continues to suggest that the observability of vibrational spectra be taken as evidence for a species. He also suggests that NMR data might be used when the Raman method is not applicable. Eigen [11] suggests various relaxation methods also, and Williams [12] believes that electronic absorption spectra should be useful. In any case some arbitrariness will persist, although a clearer picture should result.

• 5-3 Experimental Approaches

Let us briefly consider the experimental approaches used to investigate the interactions of hydrated cations with anions (or neutral molecules or other cations) in order to get a clearer picture of the difficulties just discussed.

Most measurements are made with a view toward obtaining equilibrium constants for the formation (or dissociation) of the species presumed to exist in solution. The hydrated cations themselves are often not referred to as complexes, although on occasion they are called aquo complexes. The most common process discussed can be represented by the equation

$$M^{+Z} + nL^{Z'} \rightleftharpoons ML_n{}^{+Z+nZ'}$$

where M^{+Z} is a metal ion of charge $+Z$, n is the number of associating species L (usually an integer), $L^{Z'}$ is a *ligand* with charge Z', and $ML_n{}^{+Z+nZ'}$ is the complex formed. Other representations are suggested in Chap. 4. The process is called complex formation or *ligation*. The methods of study can be conveniently classified as those which involve activity measurements and those which measure concentration.

Among the common activity methods are those involving EMF measurements and colligative properties such as freezing point. For purposes of illustration let us consider an experiment in which a two-compartment cell is used. In one compartment let us put a mixture of Fe^{++} and Fe^{3+} ions and in the other some reference electrode. Neglecting junction potentials (a problem in itself), the EMF of the cell will depend on the ratio of the activities of the Fe^{++} and Fe^{3+} ions (other factors being constant) as given by the Nernst equation. Perchlorate anions are usually used for the reference solution, assuming that they do not complex the iron species. If, now, a new species L^- is added to this compartment, the EMF measured may change. In a formal thermodynamic sense, one can only say that the relevant activities have changed. This might be due only to a change in activity coefficients of the iron species originally present or to the formation of new species that results in a change in concentration of the original iron species or to a combination of both.

If the activity coefficients of all possible species are known, then a decision on the correct explanation of the EMF change can be made. As mentioned earlier, the activity coefficients are rarely known except in very dilute solutions. If the ligand associates very strongly with one or both of the iron species, then it should be possible to use dilute solutions, and perhaps one can obtain the activity coefficients or at least extrapolate the data to infinite dilution. For simplicity, let us assume that only the species FeL^{++} forms. The equilibrium then is $Fe^{3+} + L^- \rightleftharpoons FeL^{++}$ and

$$K_{eq} = \frac{[FeL^{++}]\gamma_{FeL^{++}}}{[Fe^{3+}]\gamma_{Fe^{3+}}[L^-]\gamma_{L^-}}$$

$$\text{EMF} = E_0 - (RT/N\mathfrak{F})\ln\frac{[Fe^{3+}]\gamma_{Fe^{3+}}}{[Fe^{++}]\gamma_{Fe^{++}}}$$

If the solution is sufficiently dilute that the ionic strength principle [13] holds, one can proceed to simplify the problem. We assume that at constant ionic strength the γ values are constant. In practice an excess of a nonreacting electrolyte (often $NaClO_4$ or $LiClO_4$) is used to maintain the ionic strength. Under these conditions the EMF of the cell will give the concentration of Fe^{3+} ions at equilibrium. If the ligand and the total Fe(III) concentrations are known, one easily obtains

$$K' = K_{eq}\Gamma = \frac{K_{eq}\gamma_{Fe^{3+}}\gamma_{L^-}}{\gamma_{FeL^{++}}} = \frac{[FeL^{++}]}{[Fe^{3+}][L^-]}$$

Values of K' are obtained at several ionic strengths μ. If Γ can be expressed as a function of μ, then K' (or $\ln K'$) can be extrapolated to $\mu = 0$, where $\Gamma = 1$ and $K' = K_{eq}$.

There are at least two problems in this procedure. One has to do with the concentration range over which the ionic strength principle holds, which is often not known for certainty, and the other with the question of what the functional dependence of γ on μ is. In *very* dilute solutions the Debye-Hückel limiting law can be used and

K_{eq} can be obtained. In more concentrated solutions some extension of this law is required.[8] The problems are particularly difficult for weak (low-K) complexes, since high concentrations are required to produce an appreciable amount of complex and then the activity coefficient function is not known. Under these conditions the alternative explanations for the activity changes cannot be distinguished. The problems are not solved by making comparisons at high ionic strength, since comparisons of K values will still include differences in activity coefficients. There is great need for experimental studies on activity coefficients in concentrated mixtures of electrolytes. Even empirical correlations of γ with solution composition would be useful for extrapolation purposes.

Concentration methods include various spectral measurements such as ultraviolet and visual spectrophotometry, Raman and infrared spectroscopy, electron spin resonance (ESR), and nuclear magnetic resonance spectroscopy (NMR) plus solubility and phase distribution methods. The intensity of the absorption of energy is pretty much proportional to the concentration of species and independent of environment. The NMR absorption should be particularly good in that the nuclei involved are usually well shielded from the environment. Most of the spectral methods do show some limitations, however, in that the absorption may be influenced by environment under some conditions. If one can obtain the concentrations of the single species involved, then the concentration constant K' can be calculated. The problem of getting the thermodynamic constant K_{eq} is essentially the same as for the activity methods. Solubility and distribution experiments may measure the sums of concentrations of species and in principle give less direct information on the species themselves than the spectral methods. As mentioned several times previously, the spectral methods may be useful in defining the species even if equilibrium constants remain hard to determine.

An important question deals with the possible existence of anions which do not associate with cations at all to form chemical species. It seems clear that certain anions do not form strong (high-K_{eq}), inner-sphere complexes in general. Among these are ClO_4^-, NO_3^-, and $SO_4^=$ ions. It would appear that this question is best studied by means of some spectral method to see if species can be detected. ClO_4^- ion is generally thought to be the least likely of the common ions to form inner-sphere complexes. Constants or complexes are reported, however, for Hg(I), Hg(II), Fe(III), and Ce(III) based on spectrophotometric studies [except for Hg(I) based on EMF measurements].

Raman-spectral studies by Plane of Cornell University show no evidence for inner-sphere complexes for any cations so far studied except for In^{3+}. The reported values may refer to outer-sphere complexes. Many $SO_4^{=}$ complexes with log K_{eq} values generally less than 4 are reported. The Raman studies again provide no evidence for inner-sphere complexes. For NO_3^- ion most of the reported values of log K_{eq} are < 1, but there is Raman evidence for inner-sphere complexes of a number of cations. Perchlorate anions are usually used in complex studies as "neutral" ions to maintain the ionic strength, without complicating the system by forming complexes, and this use appears justified for the most part. The use of NO_3^- and SO_4^{2-} ions seems to be less free of difficulty. Most other common anions are believed to give rise to inner-sphere complexes, although the evidence is not always convincing.

As suggested previously, many difficulties are appreciably lessened when strong complexes are involved, and much work remains to be done on these complexes. One may also expect that the association of neutral species with cations will be less complicated by the medium effects, as may also be true when neutral species form on ion association.

• 5-4 Thermodynamic Values

When one has obtained reliable K_{eq} values, then ΔF° can be calculated for the process. Most of the current theoretical interest in complexes centers on trying to understand comparisons between complexes involving a single metal ion with various ligands or with those involving comparisons of different metal ions with the same ligand. For such comparisons, the ΔF° values at one temperature are not very useful. It is desirable to know the ΔH° and ΔS° values which make up the resultant ΔF°. ΔH° can be measured in principle either from the temperature coefficient of K_{eq} or by direct calorimetry. The former method is often used, but it has drawbacks in that the K_{eq} values may not be accurately known and also in that ΔH° may be a nonsimple function of temperature. Calorimetric methods are being employed more extensively and should give more reliable results.

The measurements are never made under standard-state conditions, and corrections for heats of dilution must be made. These are

Table 5-1 Thermodynamic quantities for some complex formation reactions

Metal ion	Complex	t, °C	log K_{eq}	ΔH, kcal mole^{-1}	ΔS, eu	Medium
Co^{++}	$Co(NH_3)^{++}$	18	−0.52	−1.66	−8.1	Variable μ
Ni^{++}	$Ni(NH_3)^{++}$	27	2.8	−4.0	−0.5	2 M NH_4NO_3
Cu^{++}	$Cu(NH_3)^{++}$	27	4.1	−5.6	0.3	2 M NH_4NO_3
Zn^{++}	$Zn(NH_3)^{++}$	27	2.3	−2.6	2.1	2 M NH_4NO_3
Cd^{++}	$Cd(NH_3)^{++}$	27	2.6	−3.5	0.5	2 M NH_4NO_3
Cu^{++}	CuF^{+}	25	0.36	−2.5	−7	$\mu = 0$
Zn^{++}	ZnF^{+}	25	1.26	2.1	13	$\mu = 0$
Fe^{3+}	FeF^{++}	25	4.90	7.5	49	$\mu = 0$
Cu^{++}	$CuCl^{+}$	25	0.11	0.6	2.5	1 M $HClO_4$
Zn^{++}	$ZnCl^{+}$	25	−0.32	0	−1.5	$\mu = 4.5$
Cd^{++}	$CdCl^{+}$	25	2.00	0.60	11.2	$\mu = 0$
Fe^{3+}	$FeCl^{++}$	25	1.48	8.5	35	$\mu = 0$
Tl^{+}	$TlBr$	25	0.88	−2.5	−4.2	$\mu = 0$
Zn^{++}	ZnI^{+}	25	−2.93	0	−13.4	$\mu = 4.5$

often relatively small, and the calorimetric $\Delta H°$ values will often be more reliable than the K_{eq} values. The $\Delta S°$ values are then calculated by $\Delta S° = (\Delta H° - \Delta F°)/T$, and these values will reflect mainly the errors in $\Delta F°$. A few values are shown in Table 5-1 to give an idea of the magnitudes involved. Some idea of the effects of ionic strength on $\Delta H°$ and $\Delta S°$ values is given by Nancollas [14] for the ion association

$$Co(NH_3)_6{}^{3+} + Br^- \rightleftharpoons Co(NH_3)_6Br^{2+}$$

In 0.3 M $NaClO_4$ solution the ΔH and ΔS values are estimated to be 0.6 kcal mole^{-1} and 5 eu less than the respective $\Delta H°$ and $\Delta S°$ values (ca. 3 kcal mole^{-1} and ca. 20 eu).

Eventually, we should like to be able to understand in detail the factors which give rise to the thermodynamic quantities for complex formation. The problem can be broken down by use of the cycle approach mentioned previously. Let us consider the following representation:

$$\begin{array}{ccccc}
Fe^{3+}(g) & + & Cl^{-}(g) & \underset{\Delta S^\circ(g)}{\overset{\Delta H^\circ(g)}{\rightleftharpoons}} & FeCl^{++}(g) \\
\Delta H_h^\circ \downarrow \Delta S_h^\circ & & \Delta H_h^\circ \downarrow \Delta S_h^\circ & & \Delta H_h^\circ \downarrow \Delta S_h^\circ \\
Fe^{3+}(aq) & + & Cl^{-}(aq) & \underset{\Delta S^\circ(aq)}{\overset{\Delta H^\circ(aq)}{\rightleftharpoons}} & FeCl^{++}(aq)
\end{array}$$

In theory we should be able to calculate $\Delta H^\circ(g)$ by means of quantum mechanics and $\Delta S^\circ(g)$ with the aid of statistical mechanics. If the hydration quantities were known, we could obtain "experimental" values for the gaseous reaction from the measured values in solution and compare them with the calculated ones. With a complete theory we would, of course, calculate all the quantities listed. Lacking this, it would still be of great interest to obtain values for the gaseous reaction, where qualitative ideas about chemical binding, etc. could be applied. Apart from the much-discussed difficulties in obtaining reliable aqueous reaction values, there remains the problem of obtaining hydration quantities for the complex species. In general, there is neither an independent experimental method for obtaining these quantities nor a reliable theoretical one. Some approximate approaches might be made, however.

If one can compare values for the formation of neutral species in series such as

$$M^{++}(aq) + L^{=}(aq) \rightleftharpoons ML(aq)$$

with either M^{++} constant and $L^{=}$ varying or vice versa, then one might expect the hydration quantities for $ML(aq)$ to be relatively small and nearly constant. For the enthalpy change we get

$$\Delta H^\circ(aq) = \Delta H^\circ(g) + \Delta H_h^\circ(ML) - \Delta H_h^\circ(M^{++}) - \Delta H_h^\circ(L^{=})$$

and differences in $\Delta H^\circ(g)$ could be obtained. A similar argument could be used to get differences in $\Delta S^\circ(g)$. Too few measured values exist to make much use of this idea. Some work along these lines has been done by Evans and Uri [15] and Nancollas [16] for entropies and by Grinberg and Yatsimirskiĭ [17] for enthalpies. Various other approaches to the use of thermodynamic data are discussed by Rossotti.[18]

An important point that has often been overlooked in considerations of ΔS° is that one should compare ΔS° values only for reactions in which the change in the number of solute species (Δn) is the same.[19] Otherwise, even the *relative* values depend on the choice of standard state.

At this point it might be worthwhile to consider briefly the question of the choice of standard state. Bent,[19] and others, have discussed the effect of choice of standard state on entropy values (a similar argument applies to free energy). On the basis of an over-simplified lattice model for solutions it is suggested that one should use mole fraction units (N) rather than molarity. The solute standard state then corresponds to a hypothetical solution with $N_{solute} = 1$. The idea is that in this way the part of the entropy dependent on concentration and geometrical configuration can be removed.

Such an approach may be more useful when more detailed statistical-mechanical models are available. Relative values of $\Delta S°$ and $\Delta F°$ for the same Δn change are not affected by the change of standard state, and $\Delta H°$ values remain the same in any case, so that no compelling argument for using other than the usual standard states seems to exist at this time. The ideas mentioned by Bent do, however, suggest some of the factors which should be considered in interpreting entropy changes.

• 5-5 Stepwise Complex Formation

It is generally agreed that in many cases a stepwise formation of complexes can occur. The pioneering work in this field is due to the Bjerrums.[20, 21] In a series such as

$$M^{+Z} + L^{-Z'} \rightleftharpoons ML^{+(+Z - Z')} \qquad K_1$$

$$ML^{+(+Z - Z')} + L^{-Z'} \rightleftharpoons ML_2{}^{+(+Z - 2Z')} \qquad K_2$$

the successive constants K_1, K_2, ... generally decrease. The ratios $\log (K_n/K_{n+1})$ are sometimes nearly constant and positive, as are the corresponding $-\Delta H_1°$, $-\Delta H_2°$, ... values. Such relations are usually found when the ligands have no charge. There are, however, quite numerous and important exceptions to this behavior as discussed by Rossotti.[18] For example, the $\log (K_3/K_4)$ value is out of line for $Fe^{3+} - Cl^-$ complexes, and this is attributed to a change from octahedral to tetrahedral coordination (or sp^3d^2 to sp^3 hybridization). Other factors considered to be of importance are π bonding, steric hindrance, crystal field effects, and unusual entropy changes. In some cases [for example, Ag(I)-ammines] negative values of $\log (K_n/K_{n+1})$ are found. Some values are shown in Table 5-2. The measurements have been made under a variety of conditions, so that the values are only approximately comparable.

Table 5-2 *Some data on successive stability constants*

Metal ion	Ligand	t, °C	log K_1	ΔH_1	log K_2	ΔH_2	log K_3	ΔH_3	log K_4	ΔH_4	log K_5	ΔH_5	log K_6	ΔH_6
Ni^{++}	NH_3	30	2.80	−4	2.24	−4	1.73	−4	1.19	−4	0.75	−4.3	0.03	−4.3
Cu^{++}	NH_3	30	4.15	−5.6	3.50	−5.5	2.89	−5.5	2.13	−5.4	−0.5	−5.2		
Ag^{+}	NH_3	25	3.37		3.84									
Zn^{++}	NH_3	30	2.37	−2.6	2.44	−3.1	2.50	−3.9	2.15	−5.2				
Cd^{++}	NH_3	30	2.65	−3.5	2.10	−3.5	1.44	−3.5	0.93	−3.5	−0.32	−3.5	1.66	−3.5
Cd^{++}	CN^-	25	5.48		5.12		4.63		3.55					
Cr^{3+}	NCS^-	50	3.1	−2.1	1.7		1.0		0.3		−0.7		−1.6	
Cd^{++}	NCS^-	25	1.39		0.59		0.60							
Cu^{++}	Cl^-	18	2.80		1.60		0.49		0.73					
Ag^{+}	Cl^-	25	3.04		2.00		0.00		0.26					
Cd^{++}	Cl^-	25	2.00	0.60	0.70	0.60	−0.59	2.65						
Fe^{3+}	Cl^-	25	1.5		0.65		−0.14		−2					
Hg^{++}	Cl^-	25	6.8		6.6		0.57		1.05					
Al^{3+}	F^-	25	6.13	1.1	5.0	0.78	3.8	0.2	2.7	0.3	1.6	−0.75	0.5	−1.5

• 5-6 Outer-Sphere Complexes

Before discussing some correlations for inner-sphere complexes we shall look at some results for outer-sphere complexes. The situation is complicated by the difficulties in deciding whether or not any association of ions involves displacement of first-sphere ligands. Smithson and Williams [12] suggest that, if the *d-d* spectral transitions in a transition-metal ion, occurring in the visible range, are not affected, then outer-sphere complexes are formed. On this basis $CoSO_4$ is an outer-sphere complex and CoS_2O_3 an inner-sphere one. It has also been suggested that outer-sphere formation constants should correlate with Z^2/r for a metal ion with a series of anions.[22]

Probably the best evidence for outer-sphere complexes comes from studies of ions in which inner-sphere substitution is slow; and thus if association is found, it must be of the outer-sphere type. Posey and Taube,[23] for example, studied the association of $SO_4^{=}$ with $Co(NH_3)_5(H_2O)^{3+}$ ions. Under the conditions of their experiments the inner-sphere ligands remained intact. The method used involved spectral measurements in the ultraviolet region. The data could be extrapolated to zero ionic strength, and their work is quite convincing as to the existence of the outer-sphere complexes. At 25 °C they found $\Delta F° = -4.53$ kcal mole^{-1}, $\Delta H° = 0.40$ kcal mole^{-1}, and $\Delta S° = 16.6$ eu. The effect is fairly large and mainly due to the entropy term.

Phipps and Plane [24] have studied association of SCN^- and $Cr(H_2O)_6^{3+}$, $Cr(NH_3)_6^{3+}$, and $Cr(NH_3)_5Cl^{++}$ ions by a similar method. The association here is quite small, with a negative $\Delta S°$ change. References are given in these works to other studies. In many cases when the first sphere is *labile* (that is, undergoes rapid substitution), it seems likely that both inner- and outer-sphere complexes exist simultaneously. The usual methods measure the total effect in general and do not distinguish the various forms. The reported K values for outer-sphere complexes range up to ca. 10^3, and thus these complexes might well interfere in measurements involving inner-sphere K values in this range.

• 5-7 Empirical Correlations

In the absence of extensive good thermodynamic data much work has been done on obtaining empirical correlations between K (or $\Delta F°$) values and various parameters. Considering first properties of the metal ions, some parameters which might be involved are charge, radius, ionization potential (IP), electronegativity (X), atomic number, and crystal field stabilization. For metals of periodic groups IA, IIA, and IIIA and a given ligand one can generally correlate log K_{eq} with a function of charge divided by radius. Similar correlations with IP and X are found.[18] On the basis of a survey of many data Irving and Williams [25] found what is often called the Irving-Williams order for bivalent metal ions of the first transition series. When the association is with O or N atoms of a ligand, the order of log K is $Mn^{++} < Fe^{++} < Co^{++} < Ni^{++} < Cu^{++} > Zn^{++}$. Some orders have been explained by using crystal field theory, but there is some question about the proper application of the theory.[18] A comparison of K_1 values for F^- complexes gives the order $Sc^{3+} > Cr^{3+} \sim Mn^{3+} > Fe^{3+} > Ga^{3+}$ (log K_1 varies from ca. 7 to 3). K_1 values for Cl^- complexes give the order $Fe^{++} > Zn^{++} > Cu^{++} > Co^{++}$ and $Fe^{3+} > Cr^{3+} > Ga^{3+}$. The situation with regard to orders of metal ions is indeed a complicated one.

With regard to correlations with various ligand properties, some factors can be mentioned here. The ability of the ligand to enter into π as well as σ bonding can be considered to be one factor increasing stability. The π bonding may be thought of as arising from either electron donation from p or d orbitals of the ligand to the metal (*normal*) or from the reverse process (*back-bonding*).[26] The normal case may most likely occur with transition-metal ions having few d electrons, and the back-bonding may be expected with metal ions having many d electrons and ligands having vacant orbitals (for example, CN^-, which forms strong complexes).

The relative stabilities (log K values) of halogen complexes have received much attention. The usual order is $F^- > Cl^- > Br^- > I^-$, but the reverse order is found for Pt(II), Cu(I), Ag(I), Hg(II), and Tl(III). Cd(II) and Bi(III) fit neither order.

Many workers have attempted to correlate complex constants with H^+ ion complex (acid) constants. Generally, plots of log K_{eq} vs. pK acid are made (see, for example, Irving and Rossotti [27]). Many factors must be considered in interpreting such correlations, which are often rather rough.

• 5-8 Chelate Complexes

So far we have considered only ligands which occupy one coordination position in the complex, the total coordination number including, generally, solvent molecules. It has been known for a long time that some ligands may occupy more than one position, and even as many as six positions in some ethylenediaminetetracetate (EDTA) complexes. Such ligands are referred to as *chelating ligands*, the process is called *chelation*, and the complexes are called *chelates*. The terminology is based on the root, which means "claw." Ligands occupying one, two, three, etc., positions are also referred to as unidentate, bidentate, tridentate, etc. The term "dentate" comes from a root that means "tooth." Typical examples of bidentate ligands are ethylenediamine (en), oxalate ion (ox) and related species.

Much interest and discussion has centered on the so-called chelate effect. This effect is based on the observation that chelates are generally more stable ($>K_{eq}$) than their nonchelate analogs [for example, $Cu(en)^{++}$ compared to $Cu(NH_3)_2{}^{++}$]. Using the usual standard states, the extra stability appears in the positive $\Delta S°$ (*aq*) terms. Various explanations are discussed by Rossotti.[18] If the $N = 1$ standard state is used, as suggested by Adamson,[28] the entropy values become slightly negative and the effect is said to be due to configurational entropy.

Some ligands appear to be able to function in more than one way with respect to chelation. $CO_3{}^{=}$ ion, for example, can be a uni- or bidentate ligand, and perhaps $SO_4{}^{=}$ ion can be also. Not much work appears to have been done on this subject.

It seems worth noting, in passing, that the EDTA complexes are very stable in general and thus very useful when complexing agents are desired. Some of these at least are sexadentate and involve bonds to the two nitrogen and four oxygen atoms that are available for octahedral coordination.

• 5-9 Polynuclear Complexes

Somewhat less work has been done on the study of polynuclear complexes that may exist in solution. We have referred to this subject in connection with hydrolysis in the preceding chapter. As was pointed out there, hydrolysis is often regarded as an example of complex formation by OH^- ion. If OH^- ions can be used in bridges in polynuclear species, it seems likely that other ligands would show similar behavior. Halide and thiocyanate ions, for example, appear to be able to bridge between metal ions.[29] There are probably polynuclear species with both OH^- and $SO_4{}^{=}$ bridges present. $IO_6{}^{5-}$ ions appear to bridge Co(III) species in solution. A rather special type of complex has been detected in a few cases. Mixtures of Cu(I) and Cu(II),

Sb(III) and Sb(V), Sn(II) and Sn(IV), and others in the presence of ligands such as Cl^- give rise to an adsorption spectrum which is not simply the sum of the individual ion spectra. The phenomenon, which has been termed "interaction absorption," [30] is presumably due to the formation of polynuclear species containing the metal in different formal oxidation states. Polynuclear species are, of course, well known in the solid state, but they may not persist in solution.

• 5-10 Mixed Complexes

Another area of recent interest deals with mixed ligand complexes. Again, many examples are known in the solid state. In solution, the identification of mixed complexes is difficult. The thermodynamics, for example, can become quite involved. Complexes such as $[Fe(SCN)Cl]^+$ and HgClBr,[31] among others, are reported. One may expect considerable activity in this area in the future.

• 5-11 Summary

We have seen that there are some major difficulties to be overcome before the complex equilibria in solution can be understood. The question of identification of species is a central one. For small and/or highly charged cations the concept of a hydrated ion is probably a valid one. While it is possible that equilibria may exist between various hydrated cations involving different coordination numbers and geometries, it seems reasonable that tetrahedral or octahedral geometries will usually be found. Complex formation may then involve replacement of H_2O by other ligands for the inner-sphere cases. One expects that a characteristic coordination number will be maintained in most cases. The ligands also will often be associated with the solvent, although less is known about this and such an effect is frequently ignored. As better methods are developed for studying hydrated species, one can expect that more information on the complex species will become available. Fairly direct physical methods, such as have been mentioned before, would seem to hold the most promise.

Even with a knowledge of species, there remain problems of obtaining reliable thermodynamic data. Ultimately a complete explanation will require that such data be available. There is need for more information on activity coefficients as well as for more calorimetric work to obtain ΔH values. Experimental results on activity coefficients of mixtures at high concentrations should be most helpful to the complex chemist. Theoretical treatments need to recognize the existence of hydrated ions and complex species and the importance of the water structure before results applicable to real solutions will be reliable.

Careful experiments and empirical correlations will still be valuable and useful in understanding and using complexes. Thermodynamic considerations should be used as a guide in making correlations. Too often, unreliable data have been used; and some correlations would not appear to be fruitful in any case.

Apart from the theoretical interest in the subjects with which this book is primarily concerned, it should be obvious that one can expect many practical consequences. So many of the physical processes we know involve aqueous solutions that the knowledge gained touches most fields. In particular, one thinks of biology and its related fields. Biochemists, for example, are already participating to a larger extent in this work.

In the next chapters, we shall consider questions having to do with the rates and mechanisms of various processes involving aqueous species. Rates and equilibria cannot really be considered as separate aspects, for both affect the observations of chemistry and, indeed, the two are related in principle. One cannot study equilibria if the time required to attain them is very long. Some common observations may not relate at all to true equilibrium but may be controlled by rate processes.

References

1. J. Lewis and R. Wilkins (eds), *Modern Coordination Chemistry*, Interscience, New York, 1960.
2. J. C. Bailar (ed), *The Chemistry of the Coordination Compounds*, Reinhold, New York, 1956.
3. F. J. C. Rossotti and H. Rossotti, *The Determination of Stability Constants*, McGraw-Hill, New York, 1961.
4. L. E. Orgel, *Transition Metal Chemistry*, Methuen, London, 1960.
5. S. Kirschner (ed), *Advances in the Chemistry of Coordination Compounds*, Macmillan, New York, 1961.
6. G. H. Nancollas, *Quart. Rev. (London)*, **14,** 402 (1960).
7. J. F. Duncan, *Australian J. Chem.*, **12,** 356 (1959).
8. H. S. Harned and B. B. Owen, *The Physical Chemistry of Electrolyte Solutions*, 3d ed., Reinhold, New York, 1958.
9. Interactions in Ionic Solutions, *Discussions Faraday Soc.*, No. **24** (1957).

10. O. Redlich and G. C. Hood, *Discussions Faraday Soc.*, No. **24,** 87 (1957).
11. M. Eigen, *Discussions Faraday Soc.*, No. **24,** 25 (1957).
12. J. Smithson and R. J. P. Williams, *J. Chem. Soc.*, 457 (1958).
13. G. N. Lewis and M. Randall, *J. Am. Chem. Soc.*, **43,** 1112 (1921).
14. G. H. Nancollas, *J. Chem. Soc.*, 1458 (1955).
15. M. G. Evans and N. Uri, *Symp. Soc. Exptl. Biol.*, **5,** 130 (1951).
16. G. H. Nancollas, *J. Chem. Soc.*, 744 (1956).
17. A. A. Grinberg and K. B. Yatsimirskiĭ, *Bull. Acad. Sci. USSR, Div. Chem. Sci. (English Transl.)*, 239 (1952).
18. F. J. C. Rossotti in *Modern Coordination Chemistry*, J. Lewis and R. G. Wilkins (eds), Interscience, New York, 1960.
19. H. A. Bent, *J. Phys. Chem.*, **60,** 123 (1956).
20. N. Bjerrum, *Z. Anorg. u. allgem. Chem.*, **119,** 179 (1921).
21. J. Bjerrum, *Metal Ammine Formation in Aqueous Solution*, Haase, Copenhagen, 1941.
22. C. W. Davies, *J. Chem. Soc.*, 1256 (1951).
23. F. A. Posey and H. Taube, *J. Am. Chem. Soc.*, **78,** 15 (1956).
24. A. L. Phipps and R. A. Plane, *J. Am. Chem. Soc.*, **79,** 2458 (1957).
25. H. Irving and R. J. P. Williams, *J. Chem. Soc.*, 3192 (1953).
26. M. J. Sienko and R. A. Plane, *Physical Inorganic Chemistry*, Benjamin, New York, 1963, Chap. 2.
27. H. Irving and H. Rossotti, *Acta. Chem. Scand.*, **10,** 72 (1956).
28. A. W. Adamson, *J. Am. Chem. Soc.*, **76,** 1578 (1954).
29. I. Leden, *Acta. Chem. Scand.*, **10,** 812 (1956).
30. J. E. Whitney and N. Davidson, *J. Am. Chem. Soc.*, **71,** 3809 (1949).
31. Y. Marcus, *Acta. Chem. Scand.*, **11,** 610, 811 (1957).

6

Rates and Mechanisms

As on equilibrium properties of complex ions, much work has been done in recent times on the kinetic aspects of ionic reactions. Very useful discussions of this subject and reaction kinetics in general can be found in several sources.[1-5] From the point of view of the inorganic chemist, the theory and experimental methods of chemical kinetics are used to try to arrive at an understanding of comparative reaction rates and reaction mechanisms. By the term "mechanism" is meant the individual steps or processes that eventually result in the formation of more or less permanent products from the reactants.

Most net reactions involve several elementary processes some of which are relatively rapid and some relatively slow. We shall be interested in the stoichiometry of the elementary processes as well as geometrical factors. It might be said at the outset that only rarely can an approximately complete picture be given for a particular reaction. We shall briefly review some aspects of theory and experiment before looking at specific reactions of interest.

• 6-1 Reaction Rate Theory

Currently, most theoretical discussions are based on the absolute-reaction rate theory developed in some detail by Eyring and co-workers.[4] We shall not be concerned with the development of this theory but shall only review some of the basic concepts. In a given net reaction, which may involve a large number of separate or simultaneous steps, there will usually be one step that is slower than the rest. This step will be the *rate-determining step.* The reacting species in this step are said to proceed toward products via the *transition state* or *activated complex.* In general, an increase in potential energy will occur as the reaction starts, the potential energy going through a maximum at the transition state and falling at least somewhat as the products form.

Presumably, other steps will also go by this process of "crossing an energy barrier," but the one(s) with the slowest rate will limit the rate of over-all reaction. Each individual step can be reversed in principle, with the detailed events being exactly reversed. This latter statement is a consequence of the principle of microscopic reversibility or detailed balancing. Analysis of the theoretical problem leads to the expression (for ideal behavior)

$$k = \frac{k^*T}{h} e^{-\Delta F^\ddagger/RT}$$

where k = specific rate constant (equal to the rate at unit concentrations)
k^* = Boltzmann's constant
h = Planck's constant
T = absolute temperature
R = gas constant
$\Delta F^\ddagger$ = free energy of activation

The $\Delta F^\ddagger$ term refers to the difference in free energy (at constant T and pressure) between the activated complex and the reactants. By making use of the usual thermodynamic relations, the above equation can be rewritten

$$k = \frac{k^*T}{h} e^{-\Delta H^\ddagger/RT} e^{\Delta S^\ddagger/R}$$

where $\Delta H^\ddagger$ and $\Delta S^\ddagger$ are the enthalpy and entropy differences between activated complex and reactants.

Strictly speaking, the quantities $\Delta F^\ddagger$, and $\Delta H^\ddagger$, and $\Delta S^\ddagger$ refer to the standard-state values $\Delta F^{\circ\ddagger}$, $\Delta H^{\circ\ddagger}$, and $\Delta S^{\circ\ddagger}$, although the superscript is usually omitted even in the rare cases when values are calculated for the reaction occurring in the standard states. The Arrhenius activation energy E_{act} used in older treatments is related to the $\Delta H^\ddagger$

value (for the usual concentration standard states) by $E_{act} = RT + \Delta H^{\ddagger} - p\,\Delta V^{\ddagger}$, where $\Delta V^{\ddagger}$ is the difference in volume between activated complex and reactants. (For reactions in solution $\Delta V^{\ddagger}$ is often taken as zero.) Also for reactions in solution the question of activity coefficients enters, as it does for equilibria. The theoretical treatment leads to the equation $k = k_0\gamma_A\gamma_B/\gamma^{\ddagger}$ for a reaction of A and B, where the γ's refer to the activity coefficients, $\gamma^{\ddagger}$ is the activity coefficient of the activated complex, and k and k_0 refer to the specific rate constants in the medium used and standard state, respectively.

The treatment of measurements is similar to that for the equilibrium constants. Generally, a constant ionic strength μ is employed; the γ values are assumed constant in an experiment. If the γ values can be expressed as a function of μ, the k values can be extrapolated to $\mu = 0$, giving k_0. The problems involved are essentially the same as for the equilibrium studies previously discussed. In order to obtain $\Delta H^{\circ\ddagger}$ and $\Delta S^{\circ\ddagger}$ values, the temperature coefficient of k_0 can be used. Usually a plot of ln (k_0/T) versus $1/T$ is made, preferably by using at least three temperatures. The curve should be a straight line with slope $= -\Delta H^{\ddagger}/R$. $\Delta S^{\ddagger}$ can then be calculated. If the rate constants are not those for the standard state, then the temperature coefficient will include the change in γ values with temperature. This change may be relatively small, so that the $\Delta H^{\ddagger}$ values may not be greatly in error; however, the $\Delta S^{\ddagger}$ values will include a term in the logarithm of the activity coefficient ratio that may not be small at all.

Thus, once again, it is strictly necessary to have the proper data if careful comparisons are to be made. The effect of external pressure on reaction rates is also given by the theory. We can write

$$\ln\left(\frac{k_2}{k_1}\right)_T = \frac{-\Delta V^{\ddagger}(P_2 - P_1)}{RT}$$

where k_2 is the specific rate constant at pressure P_2, etc. One problem here is that $\Delta V^{\ddagger}$ may be a function of pressure, which complicates the interpretation. There are also considerable experimental difficulties, since high pressures (>100 atm) are often required. In principle, the rates can be understood in terms of the $\Delta H^{\circ\ddagger}$ and $\Delta S^{\circ\ddagger}$ values in a way similar to that for the K_{eq} values. The hydration terms for the activated complex are unfortunately even less well known than for ordinary complexes. Nonetheless, even empirical correlations should use the $\Delta H^{\circ\ddagger}$ and $\Delta S^{\circ\ddagger}$ values.

• 6-2 Experimental Considerations

The goal of the experimental measurements is to obtain k_0. There are many types of methods for these studies, and they can be found in standard references (see Ref. 3, for example). The range of rates that can be studied is limited by the methods available. In recent years considerable development in extending the range of measurements has occurred. Very slow reactions might be studied by using high-specific-activity radioactive tracers so that small amounts of reaction can be detected. Very fast reactions have received more attention, a good example being the Faraday Society discussion of 1954.[6]

Apart from difficulties in measuring the rates, there is always the problem of obtaining the rate law. The rate law describes the dependence of the rate on the concentrations of reactants and products. In a simple case of reaction between A and B the expression might be rate $= k_0[\mathrm{A}][\mathrm{B}]\gamma_{\mathrm{A}}\gamma_{\mathrm{B}}/\gamma^{\ddagger}$. If the γ values are constant during the experiment, one can write rate $= k'[\mathrm{A}][\mathrm{B}]$. In general, the rate laws are more complicated; they often involve more than one term, negative exponents, fractional exponents, etc. Considerable work and care are required to be certain that an accurate rate law has been obtained. The reader is again referred to standard works [3] for details of how this may be done. Care must be taken in the interpretation of temperature or pressure effects when complex rate laws are involved, since the over-all effect will be a sum of individual ones. For example, consider the hypothetical reaction,

$$\mathrm{A} + \mathrm{B} \rightarrow \mathrm{C} + \mathrm{D}$$

if the mechanism is

$$\mathrm{A} + \mathrm{B} \rightleftharpoons \mathrm{E} \qquad \text{rapid equilibrium}$$

$$\mathrm{E} \xrightarrow{k} \mathrm{C} + \mathrm{D} \qquad \text{slow step}$$

The rate law is

$$\text{rate} = kK_{\mathrm{eq}}[\mathrm{A}][\mathrm{B}] = k'[\mathrm{A}][\mathrm{B}]$$

The measured number will be k' and

$$\left(\frac{\partial \ln k'}{\partial T}\right)_p = \left(\frac{\partial \ln k}{\partial T}\right)_p + \left(\frac{\partial \ln K_{\mathrm{eq}}}{\partial T}\right)_p = \frac{\Delta H^{\ddagger}}{RT^2} + \frac{\Delta H_{\mathrm{eq}}}{RT^2}$$

Comparisons of k, $\Delta H^{\ddagger}$, $\Delta S^{\ddagger}$, and $\Delta V^{\ddagger}$ for reactions with different rate laws (or mechanisms) are of no fundamental significance. A comparison of rates may, however, often be useful.

Once the proper rate law, k_0, $\Delta H^\ddagger$ values, etc. are obtained, an attempt can be made to postulate mechanisms for the reaction. Any mechanism must be consistent with the stoichiometry of the reaction, the rate law, and microscopic reversibility and be chemically reasonable. The latter requirement is a rather subjective one. The rate law gives information about the composition of the activated complex but does not specify the details of its formation or geometry. Thus a rate law of the form rate = $k[A][B][C]$ does not necessarily imply a three-body collision. Usually, little direct information concerning steps other than the slow one(s) is available. The result is that one rarely, if ever, gets fewer than two possible mechanisms. When several alternative mechanisms are at hand, it is sometimes possible to do additional experiments to narrow the choice. Often, as a last resort, the mechanism chosen is the simplest one consistent with the data, but this may well be a misleading procedure.

It cannot be emphasized too strongly that great care and attention to details are necessary in obtaining kinetic data. Much ingenious interpretation in the literature is marred by the absence of reliable data.

• 6-3 Stereochemistry

As in most chemical studies, a knowledge of the detailed nature of species involved is important. One aspect which deserves more attention than we have so far given it has to do with the geometrical structure of aqueous species. This aspect is closely related to the nature of the binding (or bonding) involved in the species, and the questions may be considered together. Most of the ions of interest are of the transition-metal type or are those of metals just beyond the transition metals in the periodic table. Little has been done with most of the noble-gas-type ions save for Li^+, Be^{++}, and Al^{3+}.

As we have indicated earlier, there is little direct evidence concerning the geometries of aqueous species or even the coordination number (number of ligands attached). For hydrated ions of the simpler sort it is usually assumed that the smallest cations have tetrahedral, coordination-number-4 structures and that the larger ions have octahedral, coordination-number-6 structures. Ideas about coordination numbers and geometries in solution often are based on structures found

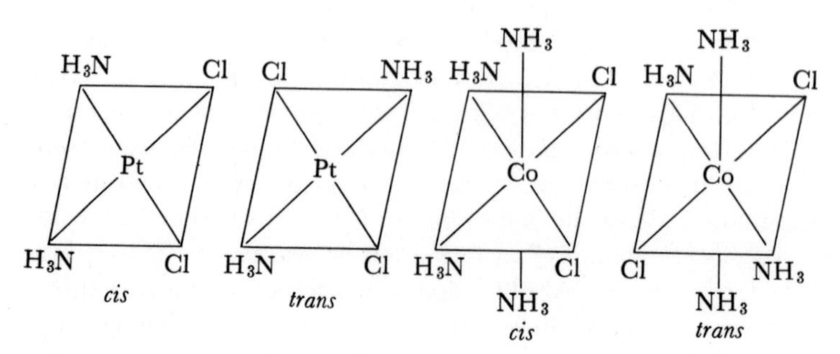

Figure 6-1 *Cis-trans isomers.*

in solids. No doubt some metal ions can exhibit more than one coordination number and geometry. In general the tetrahedral and octahedral structures are most common, but all coordination numbers from 2 to 10 are found with variable geometries. Just as in organic chemistry, isomeric forms are found under certain circumstances. There are fewer possible forms in solution than may be found in solids. The types of principal interest to us are the following:

1. Cis-trans isomers such as are found in the planar complex $Pt(NH_3)_2Cl_2$ and the octahedral complex $Co(NH_3)_4Cl_2^+$. These are usually represented as shown in Fig. 6-1, and many examples are known.

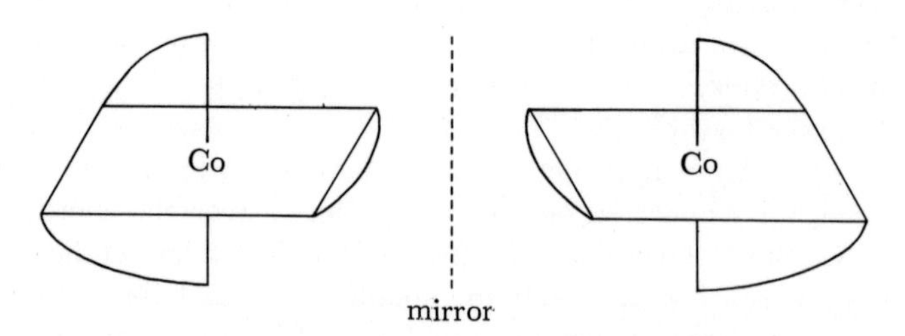

Figure 6-2 *Optical isomers of* $Co(en)_3^{3+}$.

2. Optical isomers, in which no plane of symmetry can be found in the ion, as in the octahedral complexes of Co(III) with the bidentate ligand ethylenediamine (en) usually shown as in Fig. 6-2.

A general discussion of isomerism and stereochemistry will be found in the book edited by Bailar.[7] Isomers will be of concern only when they interconvert slowly as compared to the processes with which we are dealing. It is, indeed, just those ions which undergo slow changes in their structures that give us the most information concerning the species present, as we have seen in the case of $Cr(H_2O)_6{}^{3+}$ ion. Considerably less is known about the structures of outer-sphere and polymeric complexes than is known about the structures of inner-sphere complexes.

• 6-4 Directed Valence

The stereochemistry of metal ions can be understood in terms of valence bond, molecular orbital, and crystal or ligand field theories. A detailed discussion of these theories is beyond the scope of this book, and the reader is referred to various detailed discussions.[8-10] A brief summary and review of the concepts may be useful at this point.

The valence bond picture stresses the hybridization of metal atomic orbitals to obtain directional properties. The hybrid metal orbitals then overlap ligand orbitals to form the bonds. Familiar examples are the sp^3 tetrahedral hybrids, the dsp^2 planar hybrids, and the d^2sp^3 octahedral hybrids. These limiting hybridizations will be found, in general, only when all the ligands are identical.

This picture is greatly oversimplified, but it is convenient for pictorial representations. If no d orbitals are available for hybridization (for example, Be^{++}), then tetrahedral geometry is expected in most cases. The $d_{x^2-y^2}$ and d_{z^2} orbitals are used in the d^2sp^3 hybrids. The d_{xy}, d_{xz}, and d_{yz} orbitals may be used for π bonding or may not participate in bonding at all. There are two possibilities for the octahedral hybrids, namely, nd^2nsnp^3 and $(n-1)d^2nsnp^3$, where n is the principal quantum number. The former type is sometimes called an outer-orbital hybrid, and the other is called an inner-orbital hybrid. The magnetic moment of a transition-metal ion presumably gives information about the type of hybrid involved. For example, the $Co(NH_3)_6{}^{3+}$ ion is diamagnetic, and the $CoF_6{}^{3-}$ ion is paramagnetic. This can be represented (following Pauling) as in Fig. 6-3.

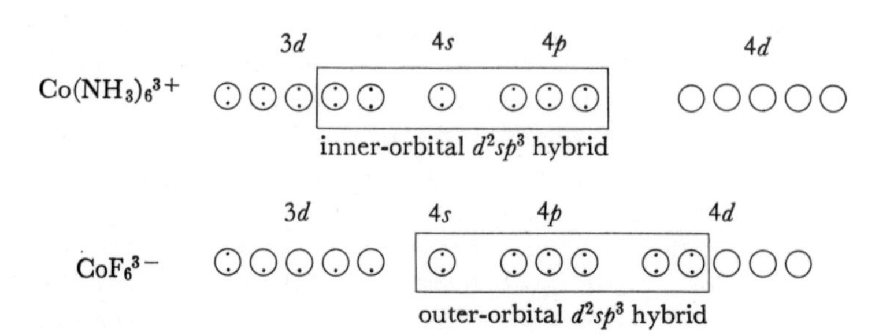

Figure 6-3 *Inner- and outer-orbital hybrids.*

Complexes in which the magnetic moment is the same as in the free ion are said to be *spin free*, and those with a lower moment are said to be *spin paired*. In general one might expect the more electronegative ligands to bond by using outer-orbital hybrids, and vice versa for ligands of low electronegativity. The various other geometries found can be accounted for by different hybridizations of the atomic orbitals. It might be noted that the older terminology, "ionic" and "covalent," has been replaced by the outer- and inner-orbital language for the most part.

The molecular orbital (MO) approach is to construct a new set of orbitals belonging to the entire molecule. This is usually done by taking a linear combination of the atomic orbitals (AO) of the metal and ligands (LCAO approximation). One obtains a number of MO's equal to the number of AO's combined, with half of these being of lower energy (called bonding) and the other half being of higher energy (called antibonding). In principle, but rarely in practice, the relative energies of these orbitals can be calculated.

A qualitative idea of the results for an octahedral complex is given by the diagram of Fig. 6-4. In this example the d_{xy}, d_{xz}, and d_{yz} orbitals are considered to be "nonbonding," although molecular π orbitals could be constructed from them and p or d orbitals of the ligands. The lower bonding levels will in general be filled by twelve electrons forming six σ bonds to the ligands. Extra electrons would then go into the nonbonding and higher antibonding levels. Up to three extra electrons go into the three nonbonding levels without pairing. If there are more than three extra electrons, the electrons will

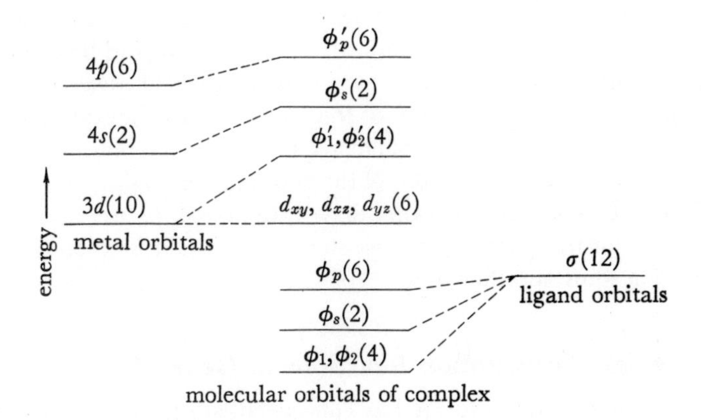

Figure 6-4 *Molecular orbitals for an octahedral complex. [From F. Basolo and R. G. Pearson, Mechanisms of Inorganic Reactions, Wiley, N.Y.,* 1958, p. 43; *reproduced with permission.*]

either pair in the nonbonding levels or go unpaired into the antibonding levels. The former case results in spin-paired complexes and the latter in spin-free complexes. The actual result depends on the relative pairing energy compared to the energy of spacing of the levels.

The magnetic properties of the ions can be understood in these terms. Spectral properties of the ions are more easily accounted for than in the valence bond theory. The absorption spectra in the visible range are explained by electronic transitions from the nonbonding (or π-bonding) levels to the antibonding levels. In the valence bond picture the stronger bonds are supposed to be formed with the inner-orbital hybrids, whereas in the MO picture the bonds are generally stronger the fewer the antibonding electrons. There are other factors (such as π bonding) that influence the net bond strengths, however, and one must be careful in trying to assess them.

The crystal field approach represents an attempt to extend the older classical electrostatic bonding theories. We have given the general outline of this point of view in the third chapter. The emphasis here is on the changes occurring in the atomic energy levels of the metal ion when the ligands are brought near the ion in some given geometrical arrangement. Spectral and magnetic properties of the ions can be accounted for in a simple way. Estimates of relative bond energies have been made (see Ref. 1, Chap. 2). The term "ligand field theory" refers to a modified crystal field theory in which MO ideas are incorporated. A readable discussion of this theory will be found in Ref. 9.

From the point of view of chemical kinetics, the binding theories should provide at least estimates of the activation enthalpies for various reactions. Basolo and Pearson [1] have attempted to use the crystal field theory for this purpose, and we shall discuss their predictions when considering some specific cases.

• 6-5 Substitution Reactions in General

Most of the work done so far has concerned substitution reactions of octahedral complexes of the transition metals. The reactions include substitution of one ligand for another or of one metal for another. Exchange reactions in which an isotopically labeled ligand or metal ion is substituted are an important special class of such reactions.

Special impetus to the study of substitution reactions was given by the classic study of Taube.[11] He made a survey of the kinetic data available and found that there were two rather clear-cut categories of behavior. In one category were the reactions essentially complete within a minute or less, while in the other were reactions which took a matter of hours. The rapidly reacting complexes were said to be labile, and the slow ones were said to be inert. The data showed no simple correlation of the rate of reaction with "stability" of the complex as measured by its formation equilibrium constant.

The most striking thing to come out of Taube's study was a correlation of substitution rates with electronic structure of the metal ion involved. The electronic structures of octahedral metal complexes can be divided into the previously mentioned inner- and outer-orbital types. As for inner-orbital complexes $[(n - 1)d^2nsnp^3]$, a striking change from labile to inert occurs when three or more extra *d* electrons are present. [The examples are all from the transition metals, and V(II) marks the change.] Most outer-orbital complexes are labile except for species in which there are high formal charges on the central atom (for example, SiF_6^{2-}, PF_6^-, SF_6).

Taube suggested that the critical factor for lability of the inner-orbital complexes was the presence of at least one vacant *d* orbital. One might suppose that the mechanism of substitution requires addition of the incoming ligand to form a coordination-number-7 activated complex. A vacant *d* orbital can bond to this ligand with a resulting lowering of the activation energy and thus a fast rate. Conversely, if no orbital is available, a high activation energy is expected. A mechanism involving loss of an original ligand to give a coordination-number-5 intermediate might be expected to require a high activation energy in any case, since the bonds are generally very strong. Taube suggests that the situation with outer-orbital complexes may be quite different in that, for ions of low charge, a dissociation mechanism may be more favorable. The picture is less clear, however, for these cases.

Basolo and Pearson [1] have attempted a more detailed explanation of the labile and inert behaviors. The simple crystal field theory is used to calculate the crystal field stabilization energy (CFSE) for regular octahedral complexes with varying numbers of *d* electrons in the weak- and strong-field cases and likewise for the regular square pyramid (coordination number 5) and the pentagonal bipyramid (coordination number 7) used as possible models for the activated complexes.

The crystal field contribution to the total activation energy is then the difference in CFSE between the original complex and activated complex. Let us take as an example the calculation of the crystal field contribution in the case of an octahedral Cr(III) complex going to a square pyramid. In the octahedral case the three $d\epsilon$ levels can each be assigned a value of -0.4Δ and the two $d\gamma$ levels can each be given the value $+0.6\Delta$, where Δ represents the energy of separation of the levels caused by the crystal field.

For a square pyramid, Basolo and Pearson [1] give the values for the *d* levels as $d_{xz} = (d_{yz})$, $-0.457\Delta'$; d_{xy}, $-0.086\Delta'$; d_{z^2}, $+0.086\Delta'$; $d_{x^2-y^2}$, $+0.914\Delta'$. The change in CFSE, then, for the Cr(III) would be $[2 \times (-0.457\Delta') - 0.086\Delta'] - 3(-0.400\Delta) = -\Delta' + 1.2\Delta$. If Δ' and Δ are approximately equal (a doubtful and hard-to-test assumption), then the net change is about $+0.2\Delta$; that is, there is a loss in CFSE that adds to the activation energy and thus slows the reaction. It must also be remembered that other factors will contribute to the total activation energy. The idea is that if ions of similar size and charge are compared, there will be some cancellation of the other factors (change in dipole moment, for example). Δ, of course, also varies from ion to ion, which must be remembered when making comparisons.

This approach in its simplest form must be regarded as rather crude but nonetheless suggestive and useful. The d^3, spin-paired d^6 and

d^8 cases show the largest crystal field contributions. The d^0, d^1, d^2, and d^{10} have no crystal field contributions at all. The latter are predicted to react more rapidly than similar complexes which do have the crystal field contribution. The general predictions on the basis of CFSE lead to nearly the same results as predicted by valence bond theory but are independent of the postulated mechanisms.

A point of some difference is that the crystal field theory predicts *relative* inertness for spin-free d^8 complexes, whereas the valence bond or Taube approach predicts only lability. Paramagnetic Ni(II) complexes are generally labile by Taube's criterion. Basolo and Pearson point out that the reactions of Ni(II) are, however, usually slower than those of Mn(II), Co(II), Cu(II), and Zn(II), which is consistent with their calculations. Comparisons should, of course, be made by using $\Delta H^\ddagger$ or E_{act} rather than the rates themselves.

Other predictions are that spin-paired d^6 complexes will have a greater $\Delta H^\ddagger$ than d^3 complexes, that spin-paired d^8 will have a lower $\Delta H^\ddagger$ than spin-paired d^6, and that for similar spin-paired complexes the order of increasing $\Delta H^\ddagger$ should be $d^5 < d^4 < d^3 < d^6$.

• 6-6 Water Exchange

Let us now consider the rates of water exchange between hydrated cations and solvent, the most fundamental sort of substitution reaction. Since isotopic exchange reactions essentially involve no net chemical change, these rates are not influenced by questions of the position of equilibrium and are closely related to the inherent rate properties of the ions. Substitutions in the inner sphere involve displacement of water molecules, and thus the rates of other substitution reactions are in principle related to rates of water exchange. If, for example, the mechanism of substitution can be represented by the hypothetical reactions

$$M(H_2O)_6{}^{n+} \rightleftharpoons M(H_2O)_5{}^{n+} + H_2O \qquad \text{fast}$$

$$M(H_2O)_5{}^{n+} + L \rightarrow M(H_2O)_5L^{n+} \qquad \text{slow}$$

then the measured rate of ligand substitution will be less than the rate of water exchange. If, however, the rate of ligand substitution is greater than the rate of water exchange, then a mechanism in which the ligand displaces the water directly is suggested.

Some detailed results [12] are reported for the exchange reaction

$$Cr(H_2O)_6^{3+} + H_2O^{18} \rightleftharpoons Cr(H_2O)_5(H_2O^{18})^{3+} + H_2O$$

Since the reacting species (H_2O) is also the solvent, it becomes nearly impossible to vary the H_2O concentration without making other drastic changes in the system. As a result, the kinetic order with respect to solvent is not known. The data are consistent with the pseudo first-order rate law, rate $= 6k[Cr(H_2O)_6^{3+}]$. The k values (which refer to the exchange of a particular H_2O in the complex) at $\mu = 0$ and 27°C are $(2.15 \pm 0.15) \times 10^{-4}$ min^{-1} and $(2.00 \pm 0.10) \times 10^{-4}$ min^{-1} for NO_3^- and ClO_4^- media, respectively. The activation energy was calculated to be 27 ± 1 kcal mole^{-1}. The exchange is very slow, the half-life for isotopic exchange being about 50 hr at $\mu = 0$ and 27°C. This behavior is consistent with other substitution reactions of Cr(III), which appear to proceed at least as slowly. There seem to be no examples in which another ligand replaces water more rapidly than water exchanges.

By using rapid mixing of the solutions in a fast-flow experiment, Baldwin and Taube [13] found that the half-life for isotopic exchange between $Al(H_2O)_6^{3+}$ and H_2O^{18} was greater than 2×10^{-2} sec.

NMR methods have been applied in different ways to get information on the rates of water exchange. Taube et al.[14] have made ingenious use of the chemical shift of H_2O^{17} in the presence of various metal ions. If the lifetime of a water molecule in a hydrated metal ion is long enough, an NMR line separate from the solvent line is expected. The authors found that for Be^{++}, Al^{3+}, and Ga^{3+} the half-times for exchange at 20°C were greater than ca. 10^{-4} sec and that for Li^+, Mg^{++}, Ba^{++}, Sn^{++}, Hg^{++}, and Bi^{3+} the half-times were less than ca. 10^{-4} sec.

Connick and co-workers [15–17] have studied the effects of paramagnetic cations on the line width of the H_2O^{17} NMR line. By means of a somewhat complicated treatment of the data, information on the kinetics of water exchange was obtained. Their results are summarized in Table 6-1. The k_1 values refer to the rate of replacement of a particular H_2O molecule. The errors in $\Delta H^\ddagger$ and $\Delta S^\ddagger$ are ca. 1 kcal mole^{-1} and 4 eu, respectively. The values in the last column come from the work of Eigen.[18] They refer to the rate of replacement of a water molecule by $SO_4^=$. These results suggest that the loss or partial loss of a water molecule is involved in the rate-determining step for $SO_4^=$ complex formation. Pearson [19] has pointed out that the proton

Table 6-1 Rate data for some fast water-exchange reactions at 25°C

Cation	k_1, sec^{-1}	$\Delta H^\ddagger$, kcal mole^{-1}	$\Delta S^\ddagger$, eu	$k SO_4^{=}$, sec^{-1}
Fe^{3+}	3×10^3	8.9	−13	
Mn^{++}	3×10^7	8.1	3	4×10^6
Fe^{++}	3×10^6	7.7	−3	
Co^{++}	1×10^6	8.0	−4	2×10^5
Ni^{++}	3×10^4	11	0.6	1×10^4

exchange between the hydrated Mn^{++} ion and the solvent is nearly the same as the rate of water exchange. The detailed considerations of Swift and Connick [17] show that the proton exchange does take place by means of loss of the whole water molecule. Swift and Connick point out that, although the general trends in k_1 values are consistent with crystal field ideas, the effects due to the crystal field are smaller than predicted by Basolo and Pearson. This is not surprising in view of the crudeness of the calculations mentioned earlier.

The rate of water exchange with $Co^{3+}(aq)$ has been investigated.[20] The exchange appears to be strongly catalyzed by the Co^{2+} ions that are present in the concentrated solutions used leading to a fast apparent exchange rate. No method has been found to remove the Co^{2+} ions completely, and the $Co^{3+}(aq)$ oxidizes water at a measurable rate and thereby makes studies difficult.

The related exchange system $Co(NH_3)_5H_2O^+$—H_2O^{18} has also been studied. It will be discussed later in this chapter.

• 6-7 Other Exchange Reactions

Many other exchange reactions have been studied in aqueous solution. The reader is referred to Basolo and Pearson [1] and Stranks and Wilkins [21] for extensive data on this subject. In general the results follow Taube's correlations as well as those of Basolo and Pearson. Rates of exchange are generally slower for chelating ligands; tridentate are slower than bidentate; and so on. In most cases detailed mechanisms have not been obtained.

It would be desirable to have extensive systematic studies comparing various cations and ligands, preferably with data referred to the usual standard states.

• 6-8 Substitution Reactions of Co(III) Complexes (Theoretical)

We shall now turn our attention to substitution reactions of octahedral Co(III) complexes, which have received a very large amount of attention. Before proceeding to some specific cases, some general considerations are in order.

The two most easily visualized mechanisms for substitution in an octahedral complex are the limiting coordination number five (CN 5) and the CN-7 mechanisms [also called S_N1(lim) and S_N2(lim)]. In the former case a ligand L is lost from the original complex *followed* by replacement by another ligand in a distinct step. In the CN-7 case a new ligand is added to the complex first, giving an expanded CN, and then another ligand leaves. These possibilities are not necessarily distinguishable on the basis of the rate law found. For example, the CN-5 mechanism shown on page 84 leads to a rate law of the form rate = $k[M(H_2O)_6{}^{n+}][L]$ (the $[H_2O]$ is essentially constant), which is the same rate law expected for a CN-7 mechanism.

If it can be definitely shown that the rate law is exactly first order in complex and zero order in all other species, then one might conclude that a dissociation process is rate-determining. Unfortunately, in aqueous solutions one can rarely, if ever, be certain that water does not play a specific role, since the dependence on water concentration is either very difficult or impossible to measure. If some additional evidence concerning the intermediate species formed can be found, a distinction could be made. In the case of a true CN-5, dissociation-limited rate, the reaction rate of a complex would be expected to be independent of the incoming ligand.

It is not necessary that the limiting mechanisms actually be the ones involved, and, in fact, it also should always be kept in mind that more than one mechanism may be operating in any case. If more than one mechanism is involved, this might be discovered by an apparent change in $\Delta H^{\ddagger}$ with temperature, since one mechanism might predominate in one part of the temperature range and would perhaps involve a different $\Delta H^{\ddagger}$.

Assuming only one mechanism, one has to consider the possibility of processes intermediate between the limiting cases just discussed. One can consider this in terms of the relative amounts of bond making and bond breaking in the activated complex. The extremes are limiting cases CN 5, where only bond breaking matters, and CN 7, where only bond making is important. It seems likely that the limiting cases may be the rarer ones. It is rather difficult to find criteria for the amount of bond making, etc., or to predict the consequences thereof. Basolo and Pearson [1] have given some predictions—strictly speaking, applicable to relative $\Delta H^{\ddagger}$ values in the gas phase—assuming an electrostatic theory for bonding.

Another important aspect involves the stereochemistry of the reaction. This is also a difficult matter about which to obtain definite information. The law of microscopic reversibility requires that for any given reaction path both forward and reverse reactions are possible. If the potential-energy curve for the reaction can be represented as in Fig. 6-5, then the incoming and outgoing groups must occupy similar or symmetrical positions in the activated complex to give a symmetrical curve near the activated complex region.

Even for the limiting cases the geometry cannot be known with any certainty. Basolo and Pearson consider a square pyramid to be most likely for CN 5 on the basis of crystal field arguments. The implications are that for a CN-5 case both the entering and leaving group are relatively far away, whereas for CN 7 both are close and possibly lying on two of the original octahedral faces. For intermediate mechanisms the picture is less clear and the CN becomes somewhat arbitrary.

The same authors also conclude on the basis of their CFSE

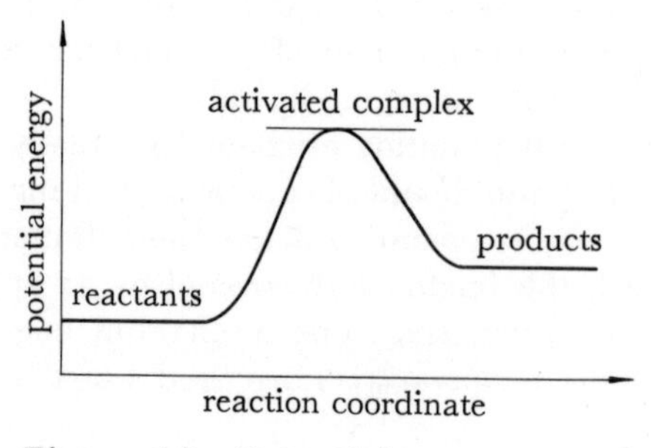

Figure 6-5 *Potential-energy curve for a chemical reaction.*

arguments that a dissociation mechanism is the most likely one or at least should have the lowest $\Delta H^{\ddagger}$. It must be noted that only a small change in $\Delta H^{\ddagger}$ is required to produce a large change in rate, so that precise rate predictions require much higher precision in estimates of $\Delta H^{\ddagger}$ than can be obtained at this time.

• 6-9 Experimental Results on Aquation of Co(III) Complexes

Let us turn now to the experimental studies on the Co(III) substitution reactions variously called aquation or acid hydrolysis. These can be represented by the general formulation

$$CoA_5L + H_2O \rightarrow CoA_5(H_2O) + L$$

In these reactions the reacting species is presumed to be H_2O rather than OH^- or H_3O^+. The evidence comes from the dependence of rate on H^+ concentration and the interpretation of the rate laws found. One expects paths involving the species H_3O^+, H_2O, and OH^- to be possible at different acidities, and often more than one path is operating, especially at moderate H^+ concentrations.

For many Co(III) reactions of the sort being considered the rates are independent of H^+ concentration below pH = ca. 4. It is these reactions we shall discuss first. The rate laws found are always of the form rate = $k_1[CoA_5L]$. The reactions are thus first order in complex concentration. They may well be pseudo-first-order reactions because of the previously mentioned problem of not being able to determine the dependence on water concentration. Thus, the rate law alone tells one very little about the reaction mechanism(s).

Two ingenious studies might be mentioned first before considering more conventional approaches. The first, by Posey and Taube,[22] involves the reaction of $Co(NH_3)_5X^{++}$ (X = Cl, Br, I) with Ag(I), Hg(II), and Tl(III) in aqueous solution leading to $Co(NH_3)_5H_2O^{3+}$. Although these are not strictly aquation reactions, the study shows how one might get information on intermediates. The reactions were carried out in water enriched in O^{18}. Any intermediate [such as $Co(NH_3)_5{}^{3+}$] formed in the reaction would be expected to react with H_2O^{16} and H_2O^{18} at different rates. By comparing the H_2O^{18}/H_2O^{16} ratio in the solvent before reaction with the same ratio found in the $Co(NH_3)_5H_2O^{3+}$ product, one can obtain the relative rates. (The complexed water exchanges slowly.) For Hg(II) the H_2O^{18}/H_2O^{16}

ratio in the product was the same for X = Cl, Br, and I and lower than in the solvent. This strongly suggests a common intermediate, namely, $Co(NH_3)_5{}^{3+}$. The ratios found with Ag(I) and Tl(III) are different from those found for Hg(II) and are not independent of X. In the case of Tl^{3+} the isotope ratio in the product is greater than in the solvent. This is explained if the water molecule in the product is carried in by the $Tl^{3+}(aq)$ ion, since O^{18} has been shown to concentrate in the hydrated ion. In this case a mechanism of intermediate character is suggested.

The second study, by H. R. Hunt and Taube,[23] involved the effect of pressure on the exchange reaction

$$Co(NH_3)_5H_2O^{3+} + H_2O^{18} \rightleftharpoons [Co(NH_3)_5H_2O^{18}]^{3+} + H_2O$$

Values found for $\Delta V^\ddagger$, $\Delta S^\ddagger$, and $\Delta H^\ddagger$ were +1.2 ml, +6.7 eu, and +26.6 kcal $mole^{-1}$. An association or CN-7 process would be expected to give a negative $\Delta V^\ddagger$. A complete dissociation is estimated to give a $\Delta V^\ddagger$ value of ca. +3.6 ml. Thus the mechanism appears to be one in which the Co—OH_2 bond is stretched considerably in the activated complex but not broken.

Let us now consider the more conventional studies on the aquation problem such as are discussed by Basolo and Pearson. The idea is to investigate various factors such as charge, size, and bonding, by systematic changes in ligands used. One can rarely, if ever, change only one factor at a time, so that the interpretations are necessarily somewhat incomplete. Often the interpretations given ignore many factors such as solvation and medium effects.

One variable that might be considered is the effect of replacing one ligand by another, similar one. Some data taken from Refs. 2 and 5 are shown in Table 6-2. A comparison of the rates for these and the few other available studies suggests the order of reactivity to be F < Cl < Br. The order of crystal field splittings (and presumably bond strengths) is F > Cl > Br, and the equilibrium constants for the formation of the aqueous complexes are also in the order F > Cl > Br. The conclusion has often been drawn from these observations that a dissociation mechanism is involved in all the reactions. An immediate difficulty is that the effects cited are small and thus automatically hard to explain. The E_{act} values do not show much difference or a general trend. It is clear also that $\Delta S^\ddagger$ effects are very important. If solvation effects are considered, it is very hard to decide between dissociation- or association-type mechanisms.[5]

Table 6-2 *Rates of aquation of some cobalt complexes at 25°C*

Complex	k, min^{-1}	E_{act}	$\Delta S^{\ddagger}$
$Co(NH_3)_5Cl^{++}$	1.0×10^{-4}	23	−9
$Co(NH_3)_5Br^{++}$	3.8×10^{-4}	24	−4
trans-$Co(en)_2F_2^{+}$	6×10^{-4}	29	+14
trans-$Co(en)_2Cl_2^{+}$	1.9×10^{-3}	27	+9
trans-$Co(en)_2Br_2^{+}$	8.4×10^{-3}	26	+9
trans-$Co(en)_2NH_3Cl^{++}$	2×10^{-5}	23.6	−11
trans-$Co(en)_2NH_3Br^{++}$	7×10^{-5}	24.6	−5.6

Another factor that is often considered is the effect of the total charge on the complex on the aquation rate. Again only limited data are available. The rate constants k (sec^{-1}) at 25°C for aquation of *cis*-$Co(en)_2(NH_3)Cl^{++}$, *cis*-$Co(en)_2Cl_2^{+}$, $Co(NH_3)_5Cl^{++}$, and *trans*-$Co(NH_3)_4Cl_2^{+}$ are 3.4×10^{-7}, 2.5×10^{-4}, 2.2×10^{-6}, and 1.8×10^{-3} (the cis complex reacts even faster), respectively. The ratios of k values between unipositive and dipositive ions are 550 and 800. Such results have been interpreted to mean that bond breaking is most important in the activated complex, since it should be easier to remove a negative ligand from the complex with the lowest positive charge. This idea ignores many other effects such as solvation and the detailed distribution of positive charge, however.

An interesting comparison would be the relative rate properties of cis and trans isomers. Most of the work has been done on Pt(II) complexes, which will be discussed later, but some comparisons are available for Co(III), as shown in Table 6-3. The data are taken from the writings of Basolo and Pearson.[5, 24, 25] In all cases but two the cis isomer reacts more rapidly than the trans isomer [the opposite is usually found for Pt(II) complexes]. Basolo and Pearson [24] have discussed the data in terms of π-bonding effects. It is interesting that the difference in the nitro complexes appears to arise in the $\Delta S^{\ddagger}$ term rather than in the $\Delta H^{\ddagger}$ term, a fact that is not so obviously explained by π bonding or its absence. There seems to be little systematic variation in either the $\Delta H^{\ddagger}$ or $\Delta S^{\ddagger}$ values, but more accurate data would help to decide this point. Basolo and Pearson [24] and Baldwin and Tobe [26] believe the results are best explained by a dissociation mechanism.

Table 6-3 *Aquation rate data for cis-trans isomers at 25°C*

Complex	k, min^{-1}	$\Delta H^\ddagger$	$\Delta S^\ddagger$
cis-$Co(NH_3)_4Cl_2^+$	>1		
trans-$Co(NH_3)_4Cl_2^+$	0.11		
cis-$Co(en)_2F_2^+$	2×10^{-4}	ca. 30	+15
trans-$Co(en)_2F_2^+$	6×10^{-4}	29	+14
cis-$Co(en)_2(OH)Cl^+$	0.78		
trans-$Co(en)_2(OH)Cl^+$	8.4×10^{-2}		
cis-$Co(en)_2(NO_2)Cl^+$	6.6×10^{-3}	22	−5
trans-$Co(en)_2(NO_2)Cl^+$	6.6×10^{-2}	22	−8
cis-$Co(en)_2Cl_2^+$	1.5×10^{-2}	22	−3
trans-$Co(en)_2Cl_2^+$	1.9×10^{-3}	27	+9
cis-$Co(en)_2(NCS)Cl^+$	6.6×10^{-4}	20.8	−14
trans-$Co(en)_2(NCS)Cl^+$	3×10^{-6}	30.4	+7.4
cis-$Co(en)_2(N_3)Cl^+$	1.2×10^{-2}	21.7	−4.2
trans-$Co(en)_2(N_3)Cl^+$	1.3×10^{-2}	23.1	+0.4

One might ask about the effects of chelation of the nonreacting ligands on the rate of replacement of X by H_2O. The bulkier these groups are, the more difficult it would appear to be for H_2O to approach the octahedron properly to displace X; thus, the CN-7 mechanism should become less favored as the groups get larger. It may also be true that the Co—X bond is altered considerably by the changes made or that the ΔH_h and ΔS_h terms are significantly changed. About all that is known is that the aquation rates decrease somewhat when two NH_3 are replaced by ethylenediamine, etc. In complexes of the *trans*-$Co(A—A)_2Cl_2^+$ type, where A—A is a bidentate ligand of the $H_2N—CR_2—CR_2—NH_2$ type, the aquation rate increases as R is varied from H to CH_3. As the chelate group gets bulkier the rate increases, which suggests a dissociation-type process.

• 6-10 Effects of Changing Central Atom

Some work has been done on effects of changing the central atom in a series of similar complexes. Replacement of an atom or ion by another of similar size and charge might be expected to have little effect on external properties (hydration, for example) but to mainly affect the electronic structure of the complex (and properties related to this structure). So far, aquation rates for unidentate complexes are pretty much limited to Co and Cr, because most other metals show very fast reactions. Cr(III) complexes usually aquate somewhat faster than Co(III) complexes, but the effect is often small. The order Co(III) > Rh(III) > Ir(III) is reported as due to increasing $\Delta H^{\ddagger}$ in the series.

The value of techniques for fast reactions is particularly apparent in attempts to make this important type of comparison. Chelating ligands may slow down the rate enough to extend the measurements to several metal ions. Data for some bidentate *o*-phenanthroline (phen) complexes are given in Table 6-4. These data confirm the predictions concerning the $\Delta H^{\ddagger}$ values based on crystal field theory [1] for a dissociation mechanism and spin-paired complexes. It will be noted, however, that the rate is greater for Fe(II) than Ni(II) in spite of the $\Delta H^{\ddagger}$ values because of the large positive $\Delta S^{\ddagger}$. The reason for the latter does not seem to be obvious. Positive $\Delta S^{\ddagger}$ values might be expected if stretching and loosening of bonds occurs in the activated complex.

Other comparisons of aquation rates might be made, but the general aspects have been covered. A lack of accurate and detailed data makes generalizations uncertain, but the results do seem to point to dissociation- rather than association-type mechanisms for the aquation reactions.

Table 6-4 *Aquation rates of o-phenanthroline complexes at 25°C* [a]

Complex	k, min^{-1}	$\Delta H^{\ddagger}$	$\Delta S^{\ddagger}$
$Fe(phen)_3^{++}$	4.3×10^{-3}	32	+25
$Co(phen)_3^{++}$	12.7	21	+5
$Ni(phen)_3^{++}$	5×10^{-4}	25	+2

[a] Data from J. Lewis and R. G. Wilkins, *Modern Coordination Chemistry*, Interscience, New York, 1960.

• 6-11 Base Hydrolysis

Another extensively studied process for octahedral complexes is the base hydrolysis reaction, which can be shown as

$$CoA_5L + OH^- \rightarrow CoA_5(OH) + L$$

The rate law found for such reactions is of the form

$$\text{rate} = k_2[\text{complex}][OH^-]$$

One must beware of jumping to the conclusion that a simple association mechanism is involved solely because of the rate law, since alternative mechanisms can lead to the same rate law. Base hydrolyses are generally very rapid compared to aquation or acid hydrolysis. This fact is certainly suggestive of a mechanism in which the OH^- displaces the ligand.

Let us look briefly at some of the same variables as were considered for aquation reactions. When the ligand being replaced is a halide ion, the base hydrolysis rate may be $>10^6$ times the aquation rate, but the order $F < Cl < Br < I$ appears to be preserved and ratios such as k_{Br}/k_{Cl} are about the same for both cases. One may be tempted to conclude that a common mechanism is operating for H_2O and OH^- as reactants, but this is not required.

Comparisons with other than halide ligands show definite differences in relative behavior between aquation and base hydrolysis. There is, of course, also no requirement that a common mechanism be found for either base hydrolysis or aquation separately, although the tendency in the literature is to hope that this at least will be so. The effect of net charge on the complex for the few examples known shows the same order as that found for aquation; that is, unipositive ions react more rapidly than bipositive ions $[Co(en)_2Cl_2^+] > [Co(en)_2(NH_3)Cl^{++}]$. One might naïvely expect the opposite order if the CN-7 (or association) mechanism were involved. On the other hand, one should also ask about the distribution of the positive charge in the complex, effects of dipole moments, solvation effects, and changes in bonding caused by the presence of different ligands.

This kind of comparison involving charge changes may be one of the least fruitful ones because of the complications mentioned. The effects of cis-trans isomerism seem to be little studied for base hydrolyses, but here the trans isomer appears to react more rapidly. Explanations for this are not given in the various review articles cited previously.

The general effect of chelation is to cause an increase in rate of base hydrolysis, a fact that has been used as evidence for a dissociation-type mechanism. Effects due to a change in the central metal atom are pretty much the same as found for the aquation reactions, where they can be studied. Most of the recent work on base hydrolysis seems to be concerned with trying to choose between an association (CN-7 or S_N2) mechanism and a conjugate base mechanism (S_N1CB).[5] The latter can be represented by the steps for a specific example:

$$Co(NH_3)_5Cl^{++} + OH^- \overset{\text{fast}}{\rightleftharpoons} Co(NH_3)_4NH_2Cl^+ + H_2O$$

$$Co(NH_3)_4NH_2Cl^+ \xrightarrow{\text{slow}} Co(NH_3)_4NH_2^{++} + Cl^-$$

$$Co(NH_3)_4NH_2^{++} + H_2O \xrightarrow{\text{fast}} Co(NH_3)_5OH^{++}$$

It may be instructive to consider some of the arguments advanced in favor of this mechanism. One such argument is that if the S_N1CB mechanism is general, then complexes without acidic protons should react much more slowly. This seems to be the case for some examples at least. The S_N1CB mechanism also predicts a rate of deuterium exchange between the complex and water more rapid than the hydrolysis. The deuterium exchange is actually about 10^5 times faster than hydrolysis. This does not rule out another mechanism but supports the S_N1CB one. Other arguments have been based on a change of solvent, but this could well cause a change in mechanism.

Although the point is probably obvious, it is clear that most of the arguments given in support of a mechanism involve the assumption that a common type of mechanism will be found. It is possible, if not pleasant, to suppose that all reactions go by different types of mechanisms. What is needed are methods of getting more direct information on the activated complexes or intermediates in the reactions. This has proved to be very difficult to do, so that resort has been to comparisons. One should keep an open mind about mechanisms, however, and try to find more definitive experiments.

• 6-12 Replacement of a Ligand by Another Ligand

It might be expected that reactions of the type

$$CoA_5X + Y \rightarrow CoA_5Y + X \qquad Y \neq OH^-$$

would be of great interest. Apparently, however, such replacement reactions proceed through a prior hydrolysis step and can be shown as

$$CoA_5X + H_2O \rightleftharpoons CoA_5(H_2O) + X$$

$$CoA_5(H_2O) + Y \rightarrow CoA_5Y + H_2O$$

It is possible that exceptions may be found by using $Y = CN^-$. The reverse reaction of aquation (second reaction above) has been called *anation*, and it has been studied quite extensively. In general a high concentration of Y is needed, since aquation is favored. If Y and the complex are charged, as is the usual case, uncertainties about ionic strength effects cause serious problems. Ion pairs may also form, and these may react at rates different from the original reactants. Not much can be said about definite mechanisms in these cases because of these difficulties.

An interesting aspect which also appears in the hydrolysis reactions has to do with ligands containing oxygen bound to the metal. For illustration, consider the process

$$Co(NH_3)_5OCO_2H^{++} + H_2O \rightleftharpoons Co(NH_3)_5H_2O^{3+} + HCO_3^-$$

One may ask whether the Co—O bond is broken or whether the C—O bond is broken. If the latter is broken, then a substitution reaction is not really involved. By using O^{18} it was shown [27] in the above case that the aquation of the bicarbonate complex did involve C—O bond breaking rather than Co—O bond breaking. In the bidentate complex $Co(NH_3)_4CO_3^+$ similar studies [28] showed that first one Co—O bond breaks and then a C—O bond. Other examples of this sort of effect have been found, so that one must be careful to keep in mind the question of which bonds are broken when comparing rates.

• 6-13 Stereochemical Changes

The last aspect of octahedral substitution we shall consider here has to do with stereochemistry. Organic chemists have made considerable use of stereochemical changes as evidence for particular activated complexes. Results on octahedral complexes offer more variety of interpretation than those on tetrahedral species, unfortunately, so less definite information can be obtained. According to Basolo and Pearson,[5] the most convincing case would be a clean-cut trans to cis conversion for which an S_N2 process involving attack on a back face of the octahedron ("trans-attack") would be the mechanism. Such an example appears to be lacking. In acid hydrolysis or aquation, cis isomers lead to cis products and some trans isomers yield cis products as well as trans products. In base hydrolysis, rearrangements are common for both cis and trans isomers.

The conversion of a cis isomer to a trans isomer is referred to as isomerization. For Co(III) complexes these reactions are usually quite slow. Kruse and Taube [29] have made an interesting study on complexes such as $Co(en)_2(H_2O)_2^{3+}$. They compared the rate of H_2O^{18} exchange with the rate of isomerization and concluded that water exchange accompanies the isomerizations but that the rates are not equal. In the case of the $Co(en)_2(H_2O)_2^{3+}$ ion the exchange corresponds approximately to one water exchanging for each cis-trans conversion. The simplest conclusion would be that the isomerization proceeds by loss of a water molecule (CN-5 mechanism), followed by rearrangement of the en ligand and then coordination of a solvent water molecule. The authors suggest that other mechanisms would also explain the results. For the $Co(en)_2(OH)_2^+$ ion less than one water molecule exchanges per isomerization and the $\Delta H^{\ddagger}$ is a function of temperature. This suggests that at least two separate paths are operating and points out another reason why temperature coefficient measurements are essential.

The process of racemization familar to students of organic chemistry also occurs in optically active inorganic complexes. Generally, the racemization rates follow the classification of complexes into inert and labile ones. Co(III) and Cr(III) complexes generally racemize slowly, as would be expected. In addition, some complexes of Fe(II), Fe(III), Zn(II) (labile class usually) have been reported to show measurable rates ($t_{1/2}$ ca. 1 min or longer). As might be anticipated, both inter- and intramolecular mechanisms have been suggested. One example cited for an intermolecular mechanism is the racemization of dextro tris- (1,10 phenanthroline) Ni(II) ion in acid solution. The rates and activation energies for dissociation of a ligand are the same as found for racemization, which seems to be sufficient evidence that the mechanisms are the same for both processes. The order with respect to solvent remains unknown as usual, so a detailed mechanism cannot be given. Isotopic exchange studies combined with studies of racemization can be of great value, as indicated in the previously discussed cis-trans isomerizations. An example is provided here by studies on $C_2^*O_4^{=}$ exchange with $Cr(C_2O_4)_3^{3-}$ compared to racemization. These show that the exchange of ligand is too slow to account for the racemization, so that an intramolecular process is indicated. The role of solvent is again not known. Considerable work has been done on optically active complexes, although mechanisms remain largely in doubt. The reader is referred to Ref. 1 for details.

• 6-14 Square Planar Complexes

Let us now turn to some aspects of substitution reactions in the spin-paired *square planar* complexes, mainly of Pt(II). In the valence bond picture the ligands are bound by dsp^2 hybrid orbitals; and for a spin-paired d^8 system no vacant lower d orbitals are available, although a p orbital is vacant. In the crystal field approach the d level energies for a square planar complex should be in the order $d_{z^2} < (d_{xz} \sim d_{yz}) < d_{xy} < d_{x^2-y^2}$ with the upper $d_{x^2-y^2}$ level vacant in Pt(II). Since this orbital points toward the ligands, it is not available to an incoming group for reaction. In fact the Pt(II) complexes belong to the class of "inert" substances as far as substitution reactions are concerned.

There is some question whether the complexes are really square planar in solution or are distorted octahedra (tetragonal symmetry) as might be expected from the Jahn-Teller effect. Presumably, solvent molecules could occupy the axial positions. There are various examples known in the solid state in which the coordination number has increased to five or six, so that the tetragonal structure may be reasonable. No usual evidence, such as the existence of isomers, cited for square planar structures is inconsistent with the distorted-octahedron picture.

One of the most studied and discussed aspects of the Pt(II) complexes is the so-called trans effect. Chernyaev suggested that a negative ligand has a labilizing effect on another ligand trans to it compared to one in a cis position. Thus, for example, the following sequence of reactions is expected:

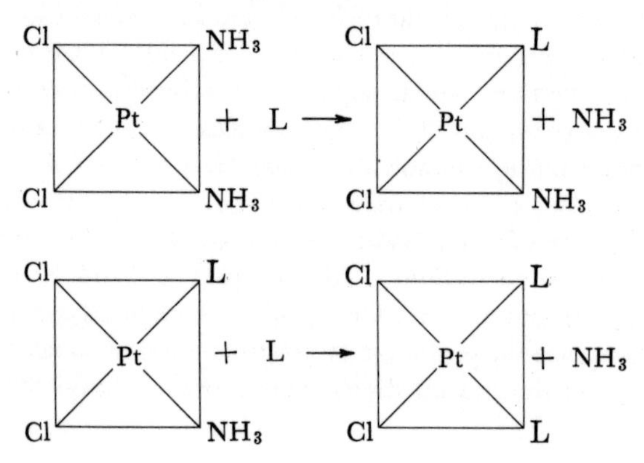

In order to account for the observations, an approximate order for the strength of the trans effect has been assigned to a variety of ligands. The order is as follows:

$$H_2O < OH^- < NH_3 < Cl^- < Br^- < I^- < PR_3 < NO < CN^-$$

for some of the ligands studied. Unfortunately, few detailed kinetic studies have been made, so that the factors responsible for the effect are usually not known. Comparisons are based on values for the rate constants. The effects are often quite small; for example, the rates of Cl^{*-} exchange for *trans*-$Pt(NH_3)_2Cl_2$ and $Pt(NH_3)_3Cl^+$ differ by about a factor of 2, and the same factor is found for acid hydrolysis of *trans*- and *cis*-$Pt(NH_3)_2Cl_2$. Even though detailed data are lacking, there is no lack of theories concerning the effect. The reader is referred to discussions in Refs. 1, 2, and 5 for details. The trans effect has found much practical use in the preparation of isomeric Pt(II) complexes.

There has been considerable interest in the possibility for π bonding in the d^8 systems. One example is given by the Pt(II) olefin complexes such as $Pt(C_2H_4)Cl_3^-$. Here the antibonding π orbitals of ethylene can accept electrons from the Pt(II) d_{xz} orbital as shown in Fig. 6-6*a*. Another example is illustrated by Fig. 6-6*b*, in which an unfilled d_{xz} level in P can accept electrons from the filled d_{xz} level in Pt, as might occur in the compound $Pt[(C_2H_5)_3P]_2Cl_2$. This type of π bonding, often called back π bonding or dative π bonding, seems to be the most likely sort for systems with a large number of d electrons. The easier replacement of ligands trans to $(C_2H_5)_3P$ ligands compared to those in cis positions has been explained by the shift in electron density away from the trans ligand because the π bonding makes it easier for incoming negative groups to replace the ligand. Presumably, a lowered activation energy compared to non-π-bonding complexes should be found. One might also expect that ligands which can accept electrons for π bonding would in general react more rapidly, since stronger bonds could form in the activated complex.

A large difficulty in obtaining data for substitution reactions of Pt(II) is that, as mentioned before, such reactions usually proceed in water by a prior aquation or base hydrolysis. The exchange of radioactive Cl^{*-} with $PtCl_4^{=}$ has been studied in some detail, and the rate of Cl^- exchange is approximately equal to the rate of hydrolysis. There

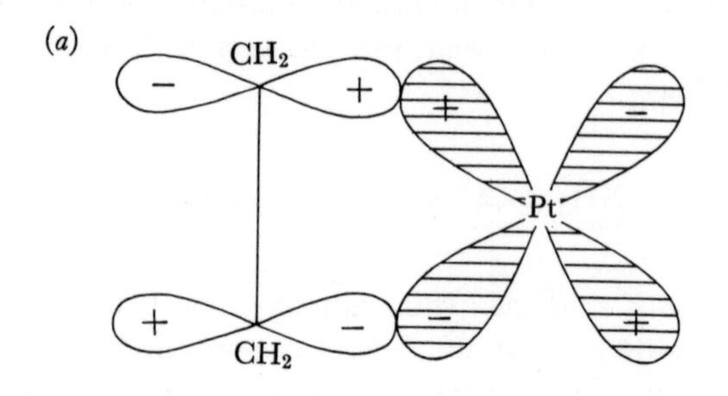

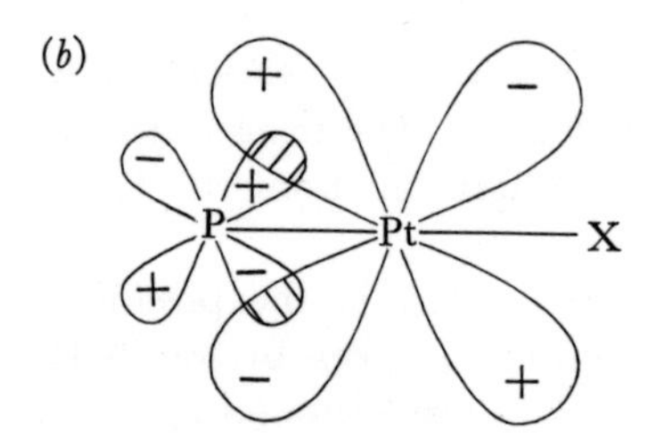

Figure 6-6 *π bonding in metal complexes.* (*a*) Pt—C_2H_4; (*b*) Pt—P.

is some evidence, though, that $Pt(H_2O)Cl_3^-$ undergoes direct Cl^{*-} exchange. For complexes of the $PtX_4^=$ type the order of exchange rates is $CN^- > I^- > Br^- > Cl^-$, which is just the reverse order of the stability constants for the complexes. From what has been said above it would appear that one is comparing hydrolysis rates.

For analogous complexes the evidence seems to be that the order of reactivity for different metals is Ni(II) > Pd(II) > Pt(II). This order is consistent with a displacement- or association-type mechanism, since Ni(II) is known to increase its coordination most readily.[5]

Although data are scarce, most authors seem to favor a displacement- or association-type mechanism for the square planar complexes largely because of the possibility of expanding the coordination number.

• 6-15 Tetrahedral Complexes

Tetrahedral complexes are generally very labile, and thus they will often require fast-reaction techniques. An example of a relatively slow reaction is the exchange of $C^{14}O$ with $Ni(CO)_4$ in toluene solution.[30] At 0°C the rate is first order in complex and independent of CO concentration. The value of k_1 is 7.5×10^{-4} sec^{-1}, and E_{act} is 13 kcal $mole^{-1}$. A dissociation mechanism is suggested. Formally, the complex contains Ni(O), and a d^{10} system is at hand with two π bonds to be distributed among four ligands. Basolo suggests that dissociation might occur because more effective π bonding is possible in a triangular planar structure.

• 6-16 Photochemistry

An important but relatively neglected area of complex reactions is that of photochemistry. Most of the recent interest has centered on complexes of the transition metals, although studies could be made whenever the metal ion or complex or the ligand shows light absorption in a usable range of wavelength. The photochemical range is generally from about 2000 to 8000 A. Below 2000 A one is in the field of radiation chemistry, and above 8000 A the energies approach thermal energies.

One reason for the interest in photochemistry is that it may offer the possibility of changing electronic structures to see the effects on rate behavior. Aqueous transition-metal ions and their complexes in general show two types of light absorption phenomena. In the visible and near-ultraviolet portions of the spectrum there are broad, low-intensity bands responsible for the colors of the species involved. These can be understood in terms of electronic transitions between the various *d* levels present ($d\epsilon$ and $d\gamma$, for example). In addition, broad, high-intensity bands are usually found in the ultraviolet. These may actually overlap the bands just mentioned. These high-intensity bands are attributed to electron transfer between metal ion and ligand or solvent and vice versa.

One might suppose naïvely that an electronic transition which makes an inner *d* orbital available would result in a labile species or that putting an electron in a $d\gamma$ level would weaken the metal-ligand bond. It would be necessary in any case that the excited state persist long enough for appreciable reaction to occur. There are quite efficient processes for deactivating excited states in solution, and thus the over-all effect may be small. Some studies which might be mentioned concern Cr(III) and Co(III) complexes (see Refs. 31 through 33 and Ref. 34, respectively). These complexes show rather different behavior. For Co(III), oxidation-reduction often occurs, whereas for Cr(III) only substitution seems to take place. Thus, $Co(NH_3)_5I^{++}$ goes to Co(II) and I_2, $Co(NH_3)_5NCS^{++}$ gives Co(II) and $Co(NH_3)_5H_2O^{3+}$ among other products, whereas only hydrolysis occurs for $Cr(NH_3)_5NCS^{++}$. $Co(NH_3)_6{}^{3+}$ apparently gives no photochemical hydrolysis, whereas $Cr(NH_3)_6{}^{3+}$ shows a quantum yield (molecules reacted per quantum) of ca. 0.4. The quantum yield for H_2O^{18} exchange with $Cr(H_2O)_6{}^{3+}$ is small, being ca. 0.02.

Adamson [33] has proposed a three-stage mechanism to explain the photochemical results. The first stage can be represented as

$$[M(III)A_5X] + h\nu \rightarrow [M(II)A_5 \cdot X] + \Delta$$

in which the bond to atom X is broken and Δ represents some form of excess energy. In the second stage, the species $[M(II)A_5 \cdot X]$ can return to the original complex or interact with the solvent:

$$[M(II)A_5 \cdot X] \rightarrow [M(III)A_5X] + \Delta'$$

or

$$[M(II)A_5 \cdot X] + H_2O \rightarrow [M(II)A_5(H_2O) \cdot X]$$

In the third stage again two possibilities exist:

$$[M(II)A_5(H_2O) \cdot X] \rightarrow [M(III)A_5H_2O] + X^-$$

or

$$[M(II)A_5(H_2O) \cdot X] \rightarrow M(II) + 5A + X^-$$

The observed results will depend on the relative importance of the various possible steps.

Plane and Hunt [31] suggest a different mechanism involving reaction of the excited molecules. In order to get a relatively long-lived excited state, they suggest that after the initial excitation the molecules fall to a doublet state of the Cr(III) complex which persists because of spin-forbiddenness. Reaction can take place in this excited state, as well as deactivation without fluorescence. Assuming such a mechanism, the activation energy for H_2O^{18} exchange by the excited species is ca. 13 kcal mole^{-1}, which is a quite reasonable value for a labile complex. In this picture the importance of a vacant $d\epsilon$ orbital is suggested. In the case of $Co(NH_3)_6{}^{3+}$ (d^6 spin-paired) no photohydrolysis is observed when the $d\epsilon$ levels each presumably still contain at least one electron

($d^2d^2d^1$), whereas for $Cr(NH_3)_6{}^{3+}$ (d^3) photohydrolysis does occur ($d\epsilon^2\ d\gamma^1$).

Work in the field of photochemistry, while not easy, should be very worthwhile to help in clarifying the role of electronic structure in determining reaction rates.

• 6-17 Hot-Atom Reactions

A rather more drastic sort of reaction than the ones so far discussed involves the "hot-atom" chemistry of complexes in solution. For purposes of illustration we shall consider some work done on $Cr(NCS)_6{}^{3-}$ ion.[35] Upon neutron bombardment the nuclear reaction Cr^{50} (n,γ) Cr^{51} occurs. The chromium nucleus will recoil, owing to conservation of momentum, when a γ ray is emitted. In addition, some of the energy released may go into ionizing electrons from the various atoms present. A maximum of 880 ev is available for various processes (thus the term "hot-atom"). One might suppose complete destruction of the complex with formation of $Cr(H_2O)_6{}^{3+}$ would occur, owing to breaking of bonds in the energy release. Actually, however, about one-third of the radioactivity is found in $Cr(H_2O)_6{}^{3+}$, one-third in $Cr(H_2O)_5(NCS)^{++}$, and most of the rest in complexes containing two NCS^- groups. It is known that many complex processes occur in hot-atom chemistry, and the details are very difficult to discover; but it seems worthwhile to extend such studies to complexes for practical as well as theoretical reasons. So far very little has been done in this area.

References

1. F. Basolo and R. G. Pearson, *Mechanisms of Inorganic Reactions*, Wiley, New York, 1958.
2. J. Lewis and R. G. Wilkins, *Modern Coordination Chemistry*, Interscience, New York, 1960.
3. S. W. Benson, *Foundations of Chemical Kinetics*, McGraw-Hill, New York, 1960.
4. S. Glasstone, K. J. Laidler, and H. Eyring, *The Theory of Rate Processes*, McGraw-Hill, New York, 1941.
5. F. Basolo and R. G. Pearson in *Advances in Inorganic Chemistry and Radiochemistry*, Vol. 3, Academic, New York, 1961.
6. The Study of Fast Reactions, *Discussions Faraday Soc.*, No. **17** (1954).
7. J. C. Bailar (ed), *The Chemistry of the Coordination Compounds*, Reinhold, New York, 1956.

8. L. Pauling, *The Nature of the Chemical Bond*, 3d ed., Cornell University Press, Ithaca, N.Y., 1960.
9. L. Orgel, *Transition Metal Chemistry*, Wiley, New York, 1960.
10. M. J. Sienko and R. A. Plane, *Physical Inorganic Chemistry*, Benjamin, New York, 1963.
11. H. Taube, *Chem. Rev.*, **50,** 69 (1952).
12. J. P. Hunt and R. A. Plane, *J. Am. Chem. Soc.*, **76,** 5960 (1954).
13. H. W. Baldwin and H. Taube, *J. Chem. Phys.*, **33,** 206 (1960).
14. J. H. Jackson, J. F. Lemons, and H. Taube, *J. Chem. Phys.*, **32,** 553 (1960).
15. R. E. Connick and R. E. Poulson, *J. Chem. Phys.*, **30,** 759 (1959).
16. R. E. Connick and E. D. Stover, *J. Phys. Chem.*, **65,** 2075 (1961).
17. T. J. Swift and R. E. Connick, *J. Chem. Phys.*, **37,** 307 (1962).
18. M. Eigen, *Z. Elektrochem.*, **64,** 115 (1960).
19. R. G. Pearson, J. Palmer, M. M. Anderson, and A. L. Allred, *Z. Elektrochem.*, **64,** 110 (1960).
20. H. L. Friedman, H. Taube, and J. P. Hunt, *J. Am. Chem. Soc.*, **73,** 4028 (1951).
21. D. R. Stranks and R. G. Wilkins, *Chem. Rev.*, **57,** 743 (1957).
22. F. A. Posey and H. Taube, *J. Am. Chem. Soc.*, **79,** 255 (1957).
23. H. R. Hunt and H. Taube, *J. Am. Chem. Soc.*, **80,** 2642 (1958).
24. R. G. Pearson and F. Basolo, *J. Am. Chem. Soc.*, **78,** 4878 (1956).
25. F. Basolo, W. R. Matoush, and R. G. Pearson, *J. Am. Chem. Soc.*, **78,** 4883 (1956).
26. M. E. Baldwin and M. L. Tobe, *J. Chem. Soc.*, 4275 (1960).
27. J. P. Hunt, A. C. Rutenberg, and H. Taube, *J. Am. Chem. Soc.*, **74,** 268 (1952).
28. F. A. Posey and H. Taube, *J. Am. Chem. Soc.*, **75,** 4099 (1953).
29. W. Kruse and H. Taube, *J. Am. Chem. Soc.*, **83,** 1280 (1961).
30. F. Basolo and A. Wojcicki, *J. Am. Chem. Soc.*, **83,** 520 (1961).
31. R. A. Plane and J. P. Hunt, *J. Am. Chem. Soc.*, **79,** 3343 (1957).
32. M. R. Edelson and R. A. Plane, *J. Phys. Chem.*, **63,** 327 (1959).
33. A. W. Adamson, *J. Inorg. Nucl. Chem.*, **13,** 275 (1960).
34. A. W. Adamson and A. H. Sporer, *J. Am. Chem. Soc.*, **80,** 3865 (1958).
35. S. Kaufman, *J. Am. Chem. Soc.*, **82,** 2963 (1960).

7

Oxidation-Reduction, or Electron Transfer, Reactions

We shall now turn our attention to a rather different aspect of metal ion reactions, that of oxidation and reduction, or electron transfer. This subject has been extensively reviewed in recent times.[1-3] The average chemist is probably more familiar with oxidation-reduction reactions than with the kinds of reactions discussed previously, although it has been only relatively recently that they have received much detailed investigation. Familiar examples of such reactions would be the following:

$$Fe^{++} + Ce(IV) \rightarrow Fe^{3+} + Ce^{3+}$$

and

$$5Fe^{++} + MnO_4^- + 8H^+ \rightarrow 5Fe^{3+} + 4H_2O + Mn^{++}$$

Formally, these are often considered to involve electron transfer between the various species, although the mechanisms are rarely specified. One should not confuse methods of balancing equations with mechanisms.

• 7-1 Equilibrium Aspects of Oxidation-Reduction

Let us briefly review the concepts of oxidation-reduction and its equilibrium aspects before proceeding to a consideration of the rates of such reactions. The concept is largely a formal one based on the assignment of oxidation numbers to atoms in various species. The oxidation numbers do not in general represent even approximate charge distributions and are highly arbitrary. They are also very convenient in classification of chemical substances and their reactions.

The terms "oxidation" and "reduction" are defined by algebraic increases or decreases, respectively, in the oxidation numbers. The changes in oxidation number are said to be caused by a loss or gain of electrons. Even in "simple" species such as $Fe^{++}(aq)$, one cannot say that an electron is directly lost from the ion, since there are many electrons in the hydrated ion. The lone pairs of the water molecules will also serve to alter the electron distribution from that imagined for a gaseous Fe^{++} ion in any case. One will need to consider these factors when trying to understand the reactions which occur. Although the reaction between ferrous ion and ceric species is said to be an oxidation reaction, the following reaction is usually not considered to be one:

$$Fe^{3+}(aq) + C_2O_4^{=} \rightarrow FeC_2O_4^{+}$$

In the former case an electron is "transferred" to the ceric species, yet to the extent that there is covalent character in the iron-oxalate bond there is also some electron transfer from oxalate to iron in the second case. Thus the distinction is not a sharp one, but rather is one of degree; and a fuzzy borderline region will exist.

The equilibrium constants or properties for oxidation-reduction reactions are usually discussed in terms of oxidation potentials. The thermodynamic relations are $\Delta F^\circ = -RT \ln K_{eq} = -N\mathfrak{F}E^\circ$. From the measured EMF of a cell it is often possible to obtain the E° value, which is the voltage of the cell when reactants and products are in the standard state, usually at 25°C. For convenience in tabulation and use of the E° values an arbitrary division of the total voltage is made by using the concept of half-reactions and setting the standard voltage for

$$\tfrac{1}{2}H_2(g) \rightarrow H^+(aq) + e$$

equal to zero. Only the sums of half-reactions to give complete reactions have any thermodynamic significance. One can compare relative values for a series of half-reactions if the other half-reaction is kept constant.

If one wishes values for real reactions not carried out under standard conditions, then the Nernst equation is needed. This well-known equation is, for simple cases,

$$E = E^\circ - \frac{RT}{N\mathfrak{F}} \ln \frac{\Pi a(\text{products})}{\Pi a(\text{reactants})}$$

where a refers to activity. A knowledge of activity coefficients is needed to use the equation accurately, but very approximate values are often obtained by assuming that activity equals concentration. The reader is referred to other works on this subject [4,5] for more information and examples of its use.

The relation between gaseous processes and those in aqueous solution is shown by the familiar cycle

$$\begin{array}{ccccccc} Na(g) & + & Cl(g) & \rightarrow & Na^+(g) & + & Cl^-(g) \\ \uparrow & & \uparrow & & \downarrow & & \downarrow \\ Na(s) & + & \frac{1}{2}Cl_2(g) & \rightarrow & Na^+(aq) & + & Cl^-(aq) \end{array}$$

A comparison of relative E° values for metals can be made by considering the free energy changes in sublimation, ionization of the gaseous atom, and hydration of the gaseous ion. The $T\,\Delta S$ terms are only a few per cent of the ΔH terms and can be neglected if large differences are being considered. Since the hydration quantities cannot be directly obtained, such cycles are often used to obtain them.

We see again that oxidation-reduction properties of aqueous ions, as is true of other properties, depend on a number of factors which need to be analyzed to explain the observations. That smooth trends in oxidation potentials are often not observed is simply a consequence of the balance of these various factors. Data for making analyses can often be found in the book by Latimer.[4]

• 7-2 Gaseous Reactions

Turning now to rates of oxidation-reduction reactions, it may be valuable to look briefly at some aspects of gaseous reactions, even though one cannot be at all certain that the results are applicable to solution processes. In the gas phase, considerable work has been done on "charge-transfer reactions" using, for example, measurements of ion drift velocity, mass spectrometry, ion-atom scattering, and other techniques. This very complicated field is described in detail by Massey and Burhop.[6] The kinds of systems of interest to us are of the type

$$Ar + Ne^+ \rightarrow Ar^+ + Ne$$

and

$$Ar + Ar^+ \rightarrow Ar^+ + Ar$$

The second type of process is much more likely than the first because of the possibility of quantum-mechanical resonance; that is, a symmetrical state, such as $Ar^+ \cdots e \cdots Ar^+$, that gives rise to equal energy products no matter which way the electron moves can be found. Under these circumstances even weak interactions will cause charge transfer.

Calculations on systems such as these can be made by quantum-mechanical methods with considerable success. Apparently, charge transfer can occur at relatively large separations (up to ca. 10 Bohr radii). The probability of simultaneous transfer of two electrons is quite large, being perhaps one-quarter to one-half that for one-electron transfer. Attempts have been made to carry over the ideas developed in this field to aqueous solutions. It is at once clear that many new complications arise. The species involved are not so clearly defined; they interact with the medium as well as each other; the medium may play specific roles in the reactions; and so on. We shall first consider some of the theoretical aspects and then turn to the experimental situation without trying to keep a sharp demarcation between theory and experiment.

• 7-3 Theoretical Treatments

Various references to theoretical treatments are given in the review by Halpern.[3] These are rather involved and somewhat difficult, so that we shall try only to sketch some of the main features. Direct electron transfer between the ions is the only mechanism that lends itself to even approximate calculations. If the electron transfer takes place between ions of the same geometry and nearly the same internuclear distances (possibly $MnO_4^{=}$–MnO_4^- is such a pair) then the $\Delta F^\ddagger$ can be calculated as

$$\Delta F^\ddagger = \Delta F^\ddagger(\text{rep}) + \Delta F^\ddagger(\text{reorg}) - RT \ln \kappa$$

where $\Delta F^\ddagger(\text{rep})$ is the free energy of repulsion between the reactants, $\Delta F^\ddagger(\text{reorg})$ is the free energy of reorganization of the solvent as the ions approach, and κ represents the probability of electron transfer across the energy barrier between reactants and products. Only approximate estimates can be made for the quantities required, but the results suggest that the reactions will be rapid in such cases.

If the reactants are not similar, then the theoretical considerations require that the $\Delta F^{\ddagger}$(reorg) term also include changes in the species to bring about a matching of energies between the reactants in order to facilitate electron transfer. Some bonds may have to be stretched and others compressed to accomplish this. One expects a higher $\Delta F^{\ddagger}$ than in the first case and thus somewhat slower reactions.

If the mechanism involves formation of chemical bonds in the activated complex, then the calculations required are those for ordinary chemical reactions that have not as yet been satisfactorily treated, although in principle the absolute reaction rate theory permits this. Some qualitative conclusions that might be drawn from the various theoretical considerations follow. Electrostatic repulsion will be a small factor unless the first coordination spheres of the ions are penetrated or the dielectric constant of the medium is low. As indicated above, the reorganization energies will be important, especially when atomic dimensions or geometries differ and also when different kinds of energy levels are involved (for example, $d\epsilon$ vs. $d\gamma$).

Ligands might be expected to differ in their ability to "conduct" electrons. The wave functions for gaseous atoms and ions can directly overlap, but in solution additional ligand overlap will be involved. One might expect ligands with delocalized electrons to be more efficient than those with localized bonds. The effect of the $\Delta F°$ for the over-all reaction is predicted to be that a negative value will produce a faster reaction than for $\Delta F° = 0$ (isotopic exchange). The argument is that for the former an excited state of the products may already match the energy of reactants, so that less or no reorganization is required initially. The free energy released when the excited products fall to the ground state then appears as part of the over-all $\Delta F°$ change. A nonreorganization process is not possible for $\Delta F° = 0$. Multiple electron transfers are expected to be possible, particularly when atom transfer accompanies electron transfer (oxygen atom or hydride ion transfer, for example).

Some mechanisms that might be suggested a priori seem rather unlikely on examination. One type of these involves production from the reducing agent of a solvated electron in solution that then adds to the oxidizing agent. Aside from the requirement for a very powerful reducing agent and the likely instability of the electron species, none of the observed rate laws in H_2O is consistent with such a formulation. A similar process in which the oxidizing agent removes an electron from the solvent would require a very powerful oxidizing agent at the least.

Taube [1] suggests classifying the known reactions into those involving an outer-sphere activated complex, a bridged activated complex, and those of uncertain classification. The outer-sphere reactions will be those in which both the oxidizing and reducing agents are inert to substitution and the electron transfer rate is more rapid than substitution. No penetration of one first coordination sphere by the other can occur in these cases. Shifts in geometry and atomic dimensions may occur during the reaction, but bonds to the central atom are not made or broken. In the bridged type, at least one reactant undergoes rapid substitution and the coordination spheres interpenetrate in the activated complex. If these conditions for the two types are not met, then the reactions will be of uncertain classification.

Much of the current interest in this field was stimulated by the rather sudden availability of radioisotopes following World War II. Reactions of the type

$$Fe^{3+} + \overset{*}{Fe}{}^{++} \rightleftharpoons \overset{*}{Fe}{}^{3+} + Fe^{++}$$

could then be studied. In principle, one reactant is mixed with a radioactive form of the other, the reaction is quenched, a separation of the species is made, and the appearance or disappearance of radioactivity is followed in one of the species. The treatment of the data leads to the rate of electron transfer.[7] Reactions in which a net chemical change occurs can be studied by conventional kinetic techniques including those for fast reactions. For the isotopic exchange example just given and for analogous ones, the ΔF° change in the reaction is nearly zero, the exchange occurring mainly because of the entropy of mixing.

• 7-4 Outer-Sphere Reaction Mechanisms

Examples of the outer-sphere type of reaction include MnO_4^-–$MnO_4^=$, $Fe(CN)_6^{3-}$–$Fe(CN)_6^{4-}$, and $Mo(CN)_8^{3-}$–$Mo(CN)_8^=$. In some cases, such as the $Co(NH_3)_6^{++}$–$Co(NH_3)_6^{3+}$ exchange, one of the reacting species is labile [Co(II) here], but the observed rate law and the poor bridging properties of the ligands make it seem likely that these reactions should be included in the outer-sphere category. Some typical data taken from Ref. 3 are given in Table 7-1. The k_2 values refer to the rate law found, rate = k_2 [oxidant][reductant]. A wide range of

Table 7-1 Kinetic data on outer-sphere electron transfer [a]

Reactants	Temp, °C	k_2, M^{-1} sec^{-1}	$\Delta H^{\ddagger}$, kcal $mole^{-1}$	$\Delta S^{\ddagger}$, eu
MnO_4^{-}–$MnO_4^{=}$	0	7×10^2	11	−9
$IrCl_6^{=}$–$IrCl_6^{3-}$	1	3×10^2		
$Fe(CN)_6^{3-}$–$Fe(CN)_6^{4-}$	4	ca. 10^3		
$Co(phen)_3^{++}$–$Co(phen)_3^{3+}$	0	1.1	17	+4
$Co(en)_3^{++}$–$Co(en)_3^{3+}$	25	5×10^{-5}	13.7	−33
$Co(NH_3)_6^{++}$–$Co(NH_3)_6^{3+}$	64.5	$< 10^{-8}$		
$Cr(dipy)_3^{++}$–$Co(NH_3)_6^{3+}$	4	7.1	13.0	−10
$Cr(dipy)_3^{++}$–$Co(NH_3)_5(H_2O)^{3+}$	4	6.5×10^2		

[a] phen = *o*-phenanthroline; dipy = dipyridyl; en = ethylenediamine.

reaction rates is represented by these data. It is rather difficult to compare the results, since the conditions under which the reactions were studied are often quite different. Very few data have been obtained for $\mu = 0$ conditions. The $MnO_4^{=}$–MnO_4^{-} reaction has been studied in basic solution, and the electron transfer proceeds without O^{18} exchange with the solvent. This reaction is quite sensitive to the nature of the cations present. One would expect the Debye-Hückel charge cloud to require readjustment on electron transfer and thus would expect to find a general effect of added salts. It is also possible that outer-sphere complexes may form and react at different rates.

A large increase in the rate is found when Cs^+ replaces Na^+, which may be due to a rather specific effect of Cs^+. It may be that the role of the positive ion is to aid in energy matching by moving along with the electron and thus reducing the unequal charge distribution and the reorganization needed. Possibly a symmetric structure forms with the Cs^+ between the anions. The cobalt systems involving phen, en, and NH_3 are rather interesting. These reactions are considerably slower than the others listed. It is likely that the bond distances are quite different in the Co(II)–Co(III) species; this might be expected to increase the activation energy compared to $MnO_4^{=}$–MnO_4^{-}.

Although the phen complex has a higher $\Delta H^{\ddagger}$ than the en complex, it reacts more rapidly because of the very large negative $\Delta S^{\ddagger}$ value for the en complex. This suggests that once the bond distances are adjusted in the phen complex the probability of electron transfer is very high. This may be connected with the delocalized nature of the electrons in the aromatic phen ligands. Considerably more data are needed before much can be said about these outer-sphere reactions. It is just these cases which might be treated in some detail theoretically, a fact that alone might provide an incentive to further study.

• 7-5 Bridged-Complex Mechanisms

The bridged-complex mechanisms have been discovered mainly by Taube and co-workers. The general principle is that one of the partners undergoes a first-sphere substitution by a ligand bound in the other partner, which then bridges the reacting species. If after reaction the ligand can be shown to be present in the first-mentioned partner, the bridge mechanism is established.

Actual systems that can be studied in this way are rather limited. Cr^{++} is an ideal reducing agent because it is labile to substitution and oxidizes to Cr(III), which is inert, so that a transfer of ligand must take place in the activated complex if at all. Cr(III) and Co(III) and Pt(IV) complexes can serve as inert oxidizing agents. A discussion of an example may serve to make the process clearer. When $Cr^{++}(aq)$ is reacted with inert $Co(NH_3)_5Cl^{++}$ in acidic solution, a fast reaction forming $Cr(H_2O)_5Cl^{++}$, $Co^{++}(aq)$, and NH_4^+ occurs. If the reaction is carried out in the presence of radioactive Cl^-, none of the radioactivity is found in the chromium complex; thus a direct transfer of Cl^- from cobalt to chromium has taken place. The reactions of Cr(III) species to add Cl^- are all too slow to account for the results in any case. In this way a large number of complexes of the type $Co(NH_3)_5L$ can be used as oxidizing agents. Similarly, $Cr(NH_3)_5L$ and $Cr(H_2O)_5X$ complexes have been extensively studied. For the Co(III) oxidizing agent, transfers of L to Cr^{++} were observed when L = F^-, Cl^-, Br^-, I^-, H_2O, OH^-, $SO_4^=$, N_3^-, NCS^-, PO_4^{3-}, $P_2O_7^{4-}$, and various anions derived from organic acids.

Similar results are found for $Cr(NH_3)_5L$ oxidations as well as for the $Cr(H_2O)_5X$ type. The reactions for the last two oxidants are a bit different than for the Co(III) examples. In a sense, the Cr(II) is acting as a catalyst for the changes

$$5H^+ + Cr(NH_3)_5L + Cr^{++}(aq) \rightarrow CrL + 5NH_4^+ + Cr^{++}(aq)$$

and

$$Cr(H_2O)_5Cl^{++} + Cr^{*++}(aq) \rightarrow Cr^{++}(aq) + Cr^*(H_2O)_5Cl^{++}$$

In the latter example radioactive chromium is used to observe the reaction. Some quantitative rate data for oxidation of $Cr^{++}(aq)$ taken from Ref. 3 are shown in Table 7-2. The rate laws are all of the form rate $= k_2[Cr^{++}][\text{oxidant}]$.

It is, perhaps, worthwhile at this point to consider mechanisms consistent with the observed rate law. This can be done conveniently by writing the following equations using a specific example:

$$Cr(NH_3)_5F^{++} + Cr(H_2O)_x^{++} \underset{k_{-1}}{\overset{k_1}{\rightleftharpoons}} [(NH_3)_5CrFCr(H_2O)_{x-1}]^{4+} + H_2O$$

$$[(NH_3)_5CrFCr(H_2O)_{x-1}]^{4+} \xrightarrow{k_2} \text{products}$$

The general rate law will be of the form

$$\text{rate} = \frac{k_1 k_2}{k_{-1} + k_2} [Cr(H_2O)_x^{++}][Cr(NH_3)_5F^{++}]$$

Table 7-2 *Kinetic data on bridged-complex electron transfer reactions of* $Cr^{++}(aq)$

Oxidant	Temp, °C	k_2, M^{-1} sec^{-1}	$\Delta H^\ddagger$, kcal mole^{-1}	$\Delta S^\ddagger$, eu
$Cr(NH_3)_5F^{++}$	25	2.7×10^{-4}	13.4	−30
$Cr(NH_3)_5Cl^{++}$	25	5.1×10^{-2}	11.1	−23
$Cr(NH_3)_5Br^{++}$	25	0.32	8.5	−33
$Cr(NH_3)_5I^{++}$	25	5.5		
$Cr(H_2O)_5F^{++}$	0	2.6×10^{-3}	13.7	−20
cis-$Cr(H_2O)_4F_2^+$	0	1.2×10^{-3}	13	−24
$Cr(H_2O)_5Cl^{++}$	0	9		
$Cr(H_2O)_5Br^{++}$	0	>60		
$Co(NH_3)_5H_2O^{3+}$	20	0.5	2.9	−52
$Co(NH_3)_5OH^{++}$	20	1.5×10^6	4.6	−18
$Co(NH_3)_5Cl^{++}$	20	$>10^3$		

Two extreme cases can be easily treated. If $k_{-1} \gg k_2$, then the expression becomes

$$\text{rate} = K_{eq}k_2[Cr(H_2O)_x^{++}]\,[Cr(NH_3)_5F^{++}]$$

where $K_{eq} = k_1/k_{-1}$ and is the equilibrium constant for the formation of the binuclear complex. In this case

$$\Delta H^{\ddagger}_{\text{over-all}} = \Delta H_{eq} + \Delta H_2^{\ddagger}$$

where ΔH_{eq} is the enthalpy change for the equilibrium reaction and $\Delta H_2^{\ddagger}$ is the activation enthalpy for the decomposition of the complex. If $k_2 \gg k_{-1}$, we get

$$\text{rate} = k_1[Cr(NH_3)_5F^{++}]\,[Cr(H_2O)_x^{++}]$$

and the rate of reaction is determined by the rate of formation of the binuclear complex (which may be the activated complex). There is usually no simple way to distinguish the extreme cases, and, of course, intermediate ones may exist. The best proof for the first alternative would be detection of the binuclear complex (an intermediate rather than an activated complex). So far these have eluded detection, which may only mean that their concentrations are low.

Another argument can be given for the formation of an intermediate when a low $\Delta H^{\ddagger}$ is observed. Based on the rather limited data for labile substitution reactions, one would expect roughly 10 kcal mole^{-1} or more for the $\Delta H^{\ddagger}$ of a direct substitution process such as the second alternative discussed above. A low value such as 3 kcal mole^{-1} could be explained by the first case if ΔH_{eq} is negative (that is, an exothermic reaction), since the observed $\Delta H^{\ddagger}_{\text{over-all}}$ is the sum (ΔH_{eq} + $\Delta H_2^{\ddagger}$). Such an example might be found in the reaction of $Co(NH_3)_5H_2O^{3+}$ listed in Table 7-2. If an intermediate is formed in the bridged-type reactions, then a simple comparison of over-all $\Delta H^{\ddagger}$ and $\Delta S^{\ddagger}$ values is not particularly meaningful without more data on the presumed equilibrium.

The data on the $Cr(III)X^{++}$ complexes (where X = halide) show that the rates are in the order $I^- > Br^- > Cl^- > F^-$ with an apparent reverse trend in the $\Delta H^{\ddagger}$ values. Since one might expect the binuclear intermediate stability to follow the order $F^- > Br^- > Cl^- > I^-$, it would appear that the $\Delta H_2^{\ddagger}$ value controls the observed order of rates in these cases.

A comparison of the mono- and bifluoro Cr(III) complexes is interesting. Both oxidants transfer *one* F^- predominately, suggesting that double bridges are not particularly advantageous. The rate parameters are, in fact, very similar.

It has been shown that groups not acting as bridging groups can also find their way into the Cr(III) product. For example, in the reaction of $Co(NH_3)_5Cl^{++}$ with $Cr^{++}(aq)$ in the presence of $P_2O_7^{4-}$ ion *both* Cl^- and $P_2O_7^{4-}$ are found in the product. The rates of reactions are also changed by such nonbridging ligands. One might postulate a bridged structure such as $[(NH_3)_5CoClCr(H_2O)_{x-2}(P_2O_7)]$ to explain these results.

One must be careful not to assume that ligand transfer is necessarily an essential part of the electron transfer reaction. The bridging group may serve in various ways to facilitate the movement of electrons. A negatively charged ligand would serve to bring the metal atoms closer and reduce repulsions. If the ligand has mobile electrons (for example, because of π bonding), then it may simply act as a "conductor." The reaction of $Cr^{++}(aq)$ and $IrCl_6^{=}$ yields $Cr(H_2O)_6^{3+}$ and $IrCl_6^{3-}$ even though a chloride bridge is believed to be involved. The binuclear intermediate simply undergoes a substitution more readily at the chromium-chlorine bond than at the iridium-chlorine bond. In the case of Pt(II)–Pt(IV) exchanges that may involve a chloride bridge, an atom transfer would not be sufficient to bring about a net two-electron transfer, so that more must be involved.

Very interesting results have been obtained by Taube and coworkers by using $Co(NH_3)_5L$, where L is an organic ligand, as the oxidant and $Cr^{++}(aq)$ as the reductant. Some results are shown in Table 7-3. In all these cases the ligand L is transferred to chromium and a bridged mechanism is indicated. In the cases of acetate and

Table 7-3 *Electron transfer with organic ligands as bridging groups*

Organic ligand	Temp, °C	k_2, M^{-1} sec^{-1}
Acetate	25	0.15
Butyrate	25	0.08
H-succinate	25	0.27
H-fumarate	25	4.9
H-oxalate	5	>20

butyrate complexes, one expects that the $Cr^{++}(aq)$ attacks the carbonyl group, probably at the oxygen not bonded to the Co(III). This can be shown schematically as follows:

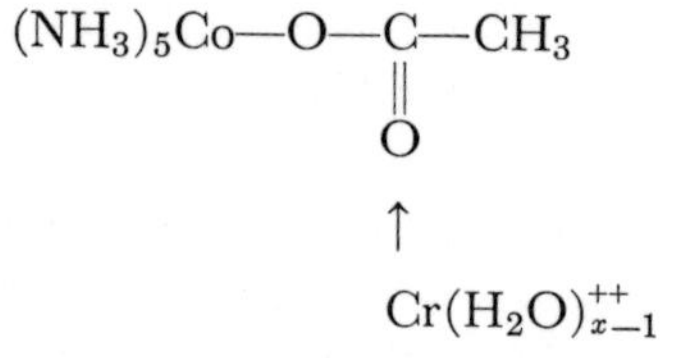

$$
\begin{array}{c}
(NH_3)_5Co—O—\underset{\underset{\displaystyle O}{\|}}{C}—CH_3 \\
\uparrow \\
Cr(H_2O)_{x-1}^{++}
\end{array}
$$

In the case of succinate ion the increased negative charge and/or the possibility of chelation may cause the enhanced rate. A comparison of fumarate and succinate is of considerable interest. These ions can be represented as follows:

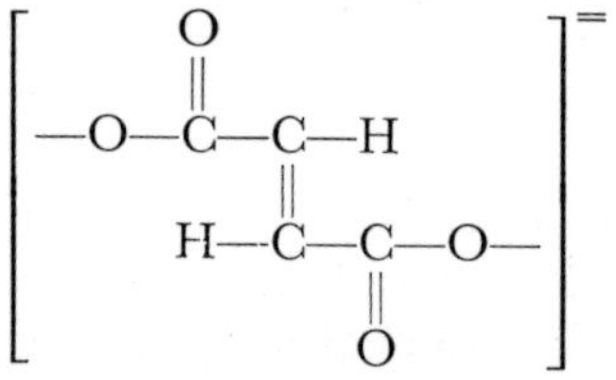

$$
\left[\begin{array}{l}
\quad\; \overset{\displaystyle O}{\overset{\|}{}} \\
—O—C—C—H \\
\qquad\;\; \| \\
\quad H—C—C—O— \\
\qquad\quad\;\;\, \| \\
\qquad\quad\;\;\, O
\end{array}\right]^{=}
\qquad
\left[\begin{array}{l}
\qquad\quad\;\; O \\
\qquad\quad\;\; \| \\
H_2—C—C—O— \\
\qquad | \\
H_2—C—C—O— \\
\qquad\quad\;\; \| \\
\qquad\quad\;\; O
\end{array}\right]^{=}
$$

fumarate 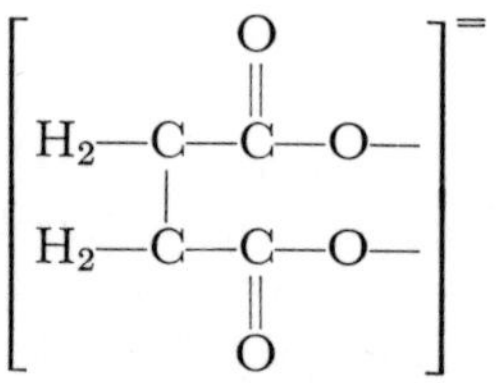 succinate

The charges are equal and fumarate cannot chelate because of its geometry, yet fumarate is the more effective ligand. Taube suggests that the explanation lies in attack of the $Cr^{++}(aq)$ at the carbonyl group remote from the Co(III), which thus avoids approach near the positive charge and yet takes advantage of the mobile electrons of the conjugated organic system. In such a case the ligand can be said to play the role of a conductor, electrons being removed at the Co(III) end and replaced by the Cr(II) at the other.

In the oxalate case, which is more rapid than the others, Taube suggests that there is a net reduction of the ligand followed by oxidation by the Co(III). This process might involve a different geometry than the conduction one. The fact that oxalate is the most easily reduced of the ligands shown is consistent with this idea. It would be desirable in all these cases to have more detailed kinetic data to check the very interesting and suggestive mechanisms which have been proposed. The reader is referred to the many papers by Taube and collaborators for details of the work on bridged mechanisms.

A factor which would be very interesting to consider is the one having to do with the electronic configurations of the species in terms of the $d\epsilon$ and $d\gamma$ populations. In the examples cited, the Cr(II) has three unpaired $d\epsilon$ electrons and one $d\gamma$ electron. The Cr(III) complexes have three unpaired $d\epsilon$ electrons, whereas Co(III) has six paired $d\epsilon$ electrons. One expects that addition or removal of electrons in $d\epsilon$ levels will have the least effect on the bonds in the complexes. Fast-reaction techniques probably will be needed for many such studies.

• 7-6 Reactions of Uncertain Mechanisms

We shall now turn to reactions whose mechanisms are in the uncertain category (perhaps "more uncertain" would be a better term). These no doubt comprise the largest group. Some representative data are given in Table 7-4. Unfortunately, the effects of ionic strength have not been systematically studied for most of these reactions, and the data are for various ionic strengths. Comparisons of $\Delta S^\ddagger$, etc. are uncertain because of this fact. The Fe(II)–Fe(III) systems have been most discussed, and considerable work has been done on them. An interesting mechanism involving H-atom transfer has been suggested.[8]

Table 7-4 *Reactions of uncertain mechanism*

Reactants	Temp, °C	k_2, M^{-1} sec^{-1}	$\Delta H^\ddagger$, kcal mole^{-1}	$\Delta S^\ddagger$, eu
V^{++}–V^{3+}	25	1.0×10^{-2}	13	−25
Cr^{++}–Cr^{3+}	25	$<2 \times 10^{-5}$		
Fe^{++}–Fe^{3+}	0	0.87	9.4	−25
Fe^{++}–$FeOH^{++}$	0	1×10^{3}	6.9	−18
Fe^{++}–FeF^{++}	0	9.7	8.6	−21
Fe^{++}–$FeF_2{}^{+}$	0	2.5	9.0	−22
Fe^{++}–$FeCl^{++}$	0	9.7	8.3	−24
Fe^{++}–$FeBr^{++}$	0	4.9	8.0	−25
Fe^{++}–$FeC_2O_4{}^{+}$	0	7×10^{2}	8.6	−14
Fe^{++}–$Fe(phen)_3{}^{3+}$	25	3.7×10^{4}	ca. 0.2	−37
Co^{++}–Co^{3+}	25	5	13	−13
V^{3+}–Fe^{3+}	25	5×10^{-3}	17	−15

This can be shown for one example as follows:

$$(H_2O)_5Fe{-}O\begin{smallmatrix} H^{++} \\ / \\ \\ \backslash \\ H \end{smallmatrix} \quad + \quad \begin{smallmatrix} H \\ \backslash \\ \\ / \\ H \end{smallmatrix}O{-}\overset{*}{Fe}(H_2O)_5{}^{3+} \rightarrow$$

$$(H_2O)_5FeOH^{++} \quad + \quad H_3O{-}\overset{*}{Fe}(H_2O)_5{}^{3+}$$

$$\rightleftharpoons \qquad\qquad \rightleftharpoons$$

$$Fe(H_2O)_6{}^{3+} + OH^- \qquad\qquad \overset{*}{Fe}(H_2O)_6{}^{++} + H_3O^+$$

In this mechanism an H atom moves from the hydrated ferrous ion to the hydrated ferric ion in the rate-determining step, the equilibria shown being rapid. The hydroxide and hydronium ions, of course, form water.

One of the arguments used in support of such a process is based on the fact that the reaction rate is reduced by a factor of 2 in D_2O compared to H_2O. A slower rate is expected if a deuterium-oxygen bond is broken. An isotope effect can result, however, without actual bond breaking and with only some stretching. Such isotope effects have been found in a number of other cases. In the reaction of $Cr^{++}(aq)$ and $Co(NH_3)_5(H_2O)^{3+}$, in which H_2O is transferred in a bridge mechanism, the ratio k_{H_2O}/k_{D_2O} is 3.8. For the likely outer-sphere case, $Cr(dipyridyl)_3{}^{++} + Co(NH_3)_5(H_2O)^{3+}$, the same ratio is 2.6. In the latter example, H-atom transfer is very unlikely and, in any case, no water is present in the reductant's inner sphere.

Thus, the isotope effects do not make any one mechanism certain. Another criterion which has been used is based on the effects caused by various added ligands. Here the reasoning must be by analogy. The Fe(II)–Fe(III) rates are increased by addition of halide ions. Several explanations might be given for this observation. It might be due to an ionic strength effect or ion-pair complexes. Either Fe(II) or Fe(III) may complex with the halide and react more rapidly because of charge reduction. A bridge might be formed between the metal ions by the halide ion as in the examples discussed earlier. The bridge might actually involve a water molecule with the halide complexed by iron but not in the bridge. Experimentally, it has been found in other studies that when the halide ion is excluded (by reason of inertness) from the inner sphere of the oxidizing agent, the catalytic effect, if any, is very small. This, by analogy, might rule out some of the possibilities mentioned above.

Particularly needed, as always, are data relating to the standard states of the reactants and products. If $\Delta H^{\circ\ddagger}$ and $\Delta S^{\circ\ddagger}$ values become available, then comparisons will be more meaningful and the arguments based on them will be more reliable. Effects of pressure may be of aid in distinguishing various mechanisms. The importance of solvation effects might be investigated by changes in the solvents used. The Fe(II)–Fe(III) reactions are slower in alcohols, and addition of water speeds up the reactions.

• 7-7 Multiple-Electron Transfers

The reactions mentioned so far have been limited to those involving a net transfer of just one electron. A number of studies have been made for systems in which a net two-electron transfer results. A new question arises here in that the process may go in a single two-electron step or in successive one-electron steps. Halpern [3] has considered two general types of such reactions. The first, called noncomplementary, is illustrated by

$$2A^+ + B^{++} \rightarrow 2A^{++} + B$$

and the second, called complementary, is depicted by

$$A + B^{++} \rightarrow A^{++} + B$$

It has been suggested that noncomplementary reactions will generally be slower than complementary ones, but Halpern has pointed out that there are many exceptions. The reaction

$$2Fe^{++} + Tl^{3+} \rightarrow 2Fe^{3+} + Tl^+$$

appears to involve successive one-electron steps. In the oxidation of Co(II) by Pb(IV) there is some evidence for an initial two-electron step to give Co(IV) and Pb(II). $Cr^{++}(aq)$ is oxidized to $Cr(H_2O)_6{}^{3+}$ by one-electron oxidizing agents such as Fe^{3+} and Cu^{++} but to a Cr(III) dimer [9] by two-electron oxidizing agents such as H_2O_2 and Tl^{3+}. The latter fact is understood if Cr(IV) forms in the initial step, since Cr(IV) should be labile and thus could form a dimer whereas Cr(III) is inert. The direct transfer of two electrons is difficult to prove or disprove for such reactions as

$$V(IV) + Tl(III) \rightarrow V(VI) + Tl(I)$$

Reactions in which H^- or O is transferred have been shown to exist, however. The reaction

$$NO_2^- + OCl^- \rightarrow NO_3^- + Cl^-$$

for example, involves oxygen atom transfer. It seems likely that some reactions between metal ions may go through a direct transfer of two electrons.

Changes involving more than two electrons in one or more of the reactants are generally thought to proceed by stepwise mechanisms involving one- or possibly two-electron transfers. The reaction

$$3Ce(IV) + Cr(III) \rightarrow 3Ce(III) + Cr(VI)$$

is thought to take place by means of the following steps:

$$Ce(IV) + Cr(III) \rightarrow Ce(III) + Cr(IV)$$

$$Ce(IV) + Cr(IV) \rightarrow Ce(III) + Cr(V)$$

$$Ce(IV) + Cr(V) \rightarrow Ce(III) + Cr(VI)$$

It seems evident that considerable work will have to be done to clear up the many details of oxidation-reduction, or electron transfer, reactions. Systematic and careful studies are needed. The use of fast-reaction techniques will greatly extend the available data. Other areas of interest will be effects of pressure, solvent changes, and attempts to detect unstable intermediates.

The field of reaction mechanisms presents one of the most fascinating tests of theoretical and experimental ingenuity in all of chemistry. A very broad spectrum of phenomena is drawn upon in order to try to elucidate the details of even simple and familiar reactions. It seems clear that no naïve approach will do; rather, the demands are for the utmost sophistication. The task is not impossible, and great strides forward have been made in recent years. Some of the significant questions to be answered are becoming clear, and this fact alone shows that considerable progress has been made.

References

1. H. Taube in *Advances in Inorganic Chemistry and Radiochemistry*, Vol. 1, H. J. Emeleus and A. G. Sharpe (eds), Academic, New York, 1959.
2. R. T. M. Fraser, *Rev. Pure Appl. Chem.*, **11,** 64 (1961).
3. J. Halpern, *Quart. Rev.* (*London*), **15,** 207 (1961).
4. W. M. Latimer, *Oxidation Potentials*, 2d ed., Prentice-Hall, Englewood Cliffs, N.J., 1952.

5. M. J. Sienko and R. A. Plane, *Physical Inorganic Chemistry*, Benjamin, New York, 1963.
6. H. S. W. Massey and E. H. S. Burhop, *Electron and Ionic Impact Phenomena*, Oxford University Press, London, 1952.
7. D. R. Stranks and R. C. Wilkins, *Chem. Rev.*, **57,** 743 (1956).
8. R. W. Dodson and N. Davidson, *J. Phys. Chem.*, **56,** 866 (1952).
9. M. Ardon and R. A. Plane, *J. Am. Chem. Soc.*, **81,** 3197 (1959).

Index